The
Chemistry
of
Carbonyl
Compounds

Prentice-Hall
Foundations of
Modern Organic Chemistry
Series

KENNETH L. RINEHART, JR., Editor

Volumes published or in preparation

N. L. ALLINGER and J. ALLINGER	**STRUCTURES OF ORGANIC MOLECULES**
TRAHANOVSKY	**FUNCTIONAL GROUPS IN ORGANIC COMPOUNDS**
STEWART	**THE INVESTIGATION OF ORGANIC REACTIONS**
SAUNDERS	**IONIC ALIPHATIC REACTIONS**
GUTSCHE	**THE CHEMISTRY OF CARBONYL COMPOUNDS**
PRYOR	**INTRODUCTION TO FREE RADICAL CHEMISTRY**
STOCK	**AROMATIC SUBSTITUTION REACTIONS**
RINEHART	**OXIDATION AND REDUCTION OF ORGANIC COMPOUNDS**
DePUY	**MOLECULAR REACTIONS AND PHOTOCHEMISTRY**
IRELAND	**ORGANIC SYNTHESIS**
DYER	**APPLICATIONS OF ABSORPTION SPECTROSCOPY OF ORGANIC COMPOUNDS**
BATES and SCHAEFER	**RESEARCH IN ORGANIC CHEMISTRY**
TAYLOR	**HETEROCYCLIC COMPOUNDS**
HILL	**COMPOUNDS OF NATURE**
BARKER	**ORGANIC CHEMISTRY OF BIOLOGICAL COMPOUNDS**
STILLE	**INDUSTRIAL ORGANIC CHEMISTRY**
RINEHART and SIM	**X-RAY CRYSTALLOGRAPHY AND MASS SPECTROMETRY OF ORGANIC COMPOUNDS**
BATTISTE	**NON-BENZENOID AROMATIC COMPOUNDS**

THE CHEMISTRY OF CARBONYL COMPOUNDS

C. David Gutsche

Professor of Chemistry
Washington University

PRENTICE-HALL, INC., ENGLEWOOD CLIFFS, N.J.

Library of Congress Catalog Card Number 66-29093
Printed in the United States of America
C-12907(p)
C-12908(c)

PRENTICE-HALL INTERNATIONAL, INC., London
PRENTICE-HALL OF AUSTRALIA PTY. LTD., Sydney
PRENTICE-HALL OF CANADA, LTD., Toronto
PRENTICE-HALL OF INDIA (PRIVATE) LTD., New Delhi
PRENTICE-HALL OF JAPAN, INC., Tokyo

Current Printing (last digit):
10   9   8   7   6   5   4   3   2

To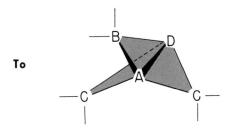

To the many students and several colleagues who were subjected to early manuscript versions of this book the author expresses his thanks admixed with apologies. Particular appreciation is extended to Drs. A. G. Hortmann, H. O. House, F. E. Mange and R. Pettit for their meticulous readings and helpful suggestions. The author is also indebted to his wife, Alice, for playing the part of the student scholar who challenged the book and worked the problems.

Foreword

Organic chemistry today is a rapidly changing subject whose almost frenetic activity is attested by the countless research papers appearing in established and new journals and by the proliferation of monographs and reviews on all aspects of the field. This expansion of knowledge poses pedagogical problems; it is difficult for a single organic chemist to be cognizant of developments over the whole field and probably no one or pair of chemists can honestly claim expertise or even competence in all the important areas of the subject.

Yet the same rapid expansion of knowledge—in theoretical organic chemistry, in stereochemistry, in reaction mechanisms, in complex organic structures, in the application of physical methods—provides a remarkable opportunity for the teacher of organic chemistry to present the subject as it really is, an active field of research in which new answers are currently being sought and found.

To take advantage of recent developments in organic chemistry and to provide an authoritative treatment of the subject at an undergraduate level, the *Foundations of Modern Organic Chemistry Series* has been established. The series consists of a number of short, authoritative books, each written at an elementary level but in depth by an organic chemistry teacher active in research and familiar with the subject of the volume. Most of the authors have published research papers in the fields on which they are writing. The books will present the topics according to current knowledge of the field, and individual volumes will be revised as often as necessary to take account of subsequent developments.

The basic organization of the series is according to reaction type, rather than along the more classical lines of compound class. The first ten volumes in the series constitute a core of the material covered in nearly every one-year organic chemistry course. Of these ten, the first three are a general introduction to organic chemistry and provide a background for the next six, which deal with specific types of reactions and may be covered in any order. Each of the reaction types is presented from an elementary viewpoint, but in a depth not possible in conventional textbooks. The teacher can decide how much of a volume to cover. The tenth examines the problem of organic synthesis, employing and tying together the reactions previously studied.

The remaining volumes provide for the enormous flexibility of the series. These cover topics which are important to students of organic chemistry and are sometimes treated in the first organic course, sometimes in an intermediate course. Some teachers will wish to cover a number of these books in the one-year course; others will wish to assign some of them as outside reading; a complete intermediate organic course could be based on the eight "topics" texts taken together.

The series approach to undergraduate organic chemistry offers then the considerable advantage of an authoritative treatment by teachers active in research, of frequent revision of the most active areas, of a treatment in depth of the most fundamental material, and of nearly complete flexibility in choice of topics to be covered. Individually the volumes of the Foundations of Modern Organic Chemistry provide introductions in depth to basic areas of organic chemistry; together they comprise a contemporary survey of organic chemistry at an undergraduate level.

KENNETH L. RINEHART, JR.

University of Illinois

Contents

1

THE STRUCTURE AND PROPERTIES OF
CARBONYL COMPOUNDS   1

2

MECHANISMS OF NUCLEOPHILIC ADDITION AND ADDITION-ELIMINATION REACTIONS OF CARBONYL COMPOUNDS 24

3

NUCLEOPHILIC ADDITION AND ADDITION-ELIMINATION REACTIONS WITH HETERO ATOM NUCLEOPHILES AND HYDRIDE ION 45

4

NUCLEOPHILIC ADDITION AND ADDITION-ELIMINATION REACTIONS WITH CARBON NUCLEOPHILES 71

5

(Elimination)

ELECTROPHILIC DISPLACEMENT REACTIONS WITH CARBONYL COMPOUNDS   100

6

OTHER REACTIONS OF CARBONYL COMPOUNDS   113

SUMMARY OF SYNTHESIS METHODS FOR CARBONYL COMPOUNDS   126

INDEX   135

The
Chemistry
of
Carbonyl
Compounds

1

The Structure and Properties of Carbonyl Compounds

$Se's$ $(+S \; or \; st.)$

$$\underset{O}{\overset{\|}{C}} = O$$

1.1 INTRODUCTION

Between carbon in its elemental state, as represented by graphite or diamond, and carbon in its most oxidized state, as represented by carbon dioxide, there exist many families of carbon-containing compounds which comprise the class of substances known as organic. Among these families, the one which probably has the greatest membership, and which for that reason claims a central place in organic chemistry, contains carbon in a partially oxidized state represented by the general formula $\overset{X}{\underset{Y}{\diagdown}}C{=}O$.

The C=O entity is called a "carbonyl group," and the members of the family of compounds containing this group are called "carbonyl compounds." In all but a very few of the members, at least one of the X and Y groups contains carbon atoms, and in most instances the link between the carbonyl group and at least one of the X or Y groups is a carbon-carbon bond.

1.2 CLASSIFICATION OF CARBONYL COMPOUNDS

As an aid to the subsequent discussion, a classification scheme will be employed in which the types of attached groups $\Big($ i.e., X and Y in $\overset{X}{\underset{Y}{\diagdown}}C{=}O\Big)$ are designated as follows:

Type A: Hydrogen *or* an organic function in which the carbon directly attached to the C=O is sp^3 hybridized. This includes hydrogen, alkyl

1

groups such as CH_3, CH_3CH_2, $(CH_3)_2CH$, $(CH_3)_3C$, and substituted alkyl groups such as $C_6H_5CH_2$, $CH_2{=}CHCH_2$, Cl_3C, etc.

Type B: Functions in which the carbon directly attached to the C=O is part of a carbon-carbon pi-bond system. This includes C=C, C≡C,

and ⟨◯⟩—

Type C: Functions in which the atom directly attached to the C=O carries non-bonding electrons. This includes HO—, RO—, H_2N—, R_2N—, HS—, RS—, halogen, etc.

Type D: Functions in which X and Y are the identical atom. This includes oxygen itself and nitrogen-containing and carbon-containing moieties which can be doubly bonded to C=O.

Various combinations of groups attached to the carbonyl function produce the several varieties of carbonyl compounds familiar to the organic chemist.[†] Thus, simple aldehydes and ketones such as acetalde-hyde and acetone are representatives of class AA compounds. α,β-Un-saturated aldehydes and ketones such as acrolein and methyl vinyl ketone as well as aromatic aldehydes and ketones such as benzaldehyde and acetophenone are representatives of class AB compounds. Representa-tives of class BB compounds include *bis*-α,β-unsaturated ketones, quinones, and diaryl ketones such as benzophenone. Carboxylic acids such as acetic acid and the various carboxylic acid derivatives including acid halides, anhydrides, esters, lactones, amides, and lactams are all representatives of class AC compounds, while α,β-unsaturated carboxylic acids and derivatives and aromatic carboxylic acids and derivatives are representatives of class BC compounds. Compounds of class CC are essentially inorganic in the vicinity of the carbonyl group and qualify as organic compounds only by possessing organic residues somewhere in the type C group; included in this class are carbonates, haloformates, ureas, and urethans. Finally, compounds such as isocyanates and ketenes are representatives of class D.

It is urged that the student dwell for a few minutes on these designa-tions and commit them to memory. This classification system, although artificial and arbitrary, is simple enough to be remembered without undue pain and will be seen to be a most useful categorizing device in the ensuing discussions of the physical and chemical properties of carbonyl com-pounds.

1.3 PROLIFERATION OF CARBONYL COMPOUNDS

As a result of the ability of the carbonyl group to be combined with a great variety of functions, carbonyl compounds have proliferated

[†] See N. L. Allinger and J. Allinger, *Structures of Organic Molecules* (Englewood Cliffs, N.J.: Prentice-Hall, Inc., 1965).

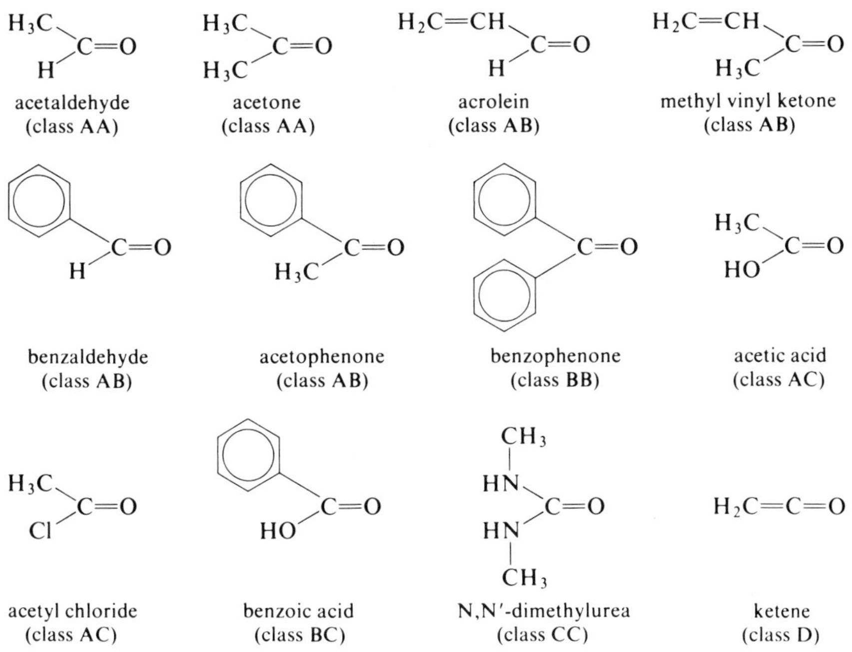

$$H_3C \quad C=O \quad H$$
acetaldehyde
(class AA)

$$H_3C \quad C=O \quad H_3C$$
acetone
(class AA)

$$H_2C=CH \quad C=O \quad H$$
acrolein
(class AB)

$$H_2C=CH \quad C=O \quad H_3C$$
methyl vinyl ketone
(class AB)

benzaldehyde
(class AB)

acetophenone
(class AB)

benzophenone
(class BB)

$$H_3C \quad C=O \quad HO$$
acetic acid
(class AC)

$$H_3C \quad C=O \quad Cl$$
acetyl chloride
(class AC)

benzoic acid
(class BC)

N,N'-dimethylurea
(class CC)

$$H_2C=C=O$$
ketene
(class D)

Fig. 1-1 Representative carbonyl compounds.

throughout the organic chemical world. Carbohydrates contain aldehyde and ketone groups, fatty acids contain carboxyl groups, fats and oils contain ester groups, and proteins contain carboxamide groups. Carbonyl functions appear in various other naturally occurring substances as well, including certain steriods (e.g., cortisone), some of the vitamins (e.g., pyridoxal, pantothenic acid, biotin, and vitamin K), some of the antibiotics (e.g., penicillin), and many of the terpenes (e.g., camphor). Many industrial products, including certain dyestuffs, several of the synthetic fibers (e.g., Nylon and Dacron), and numerous medicinals (e.g., aspirin) contain the carbonyl group. To study the carbonyl group in its various chemical combinations, then, is to study a central portion of organic chemistry. To understand the behavior of carbonyl compounds is to understand a large segment of organic chemistry.

1.4 HOW TO READ THIS BOOK

Suggestions of how to read a book are frequently presented in the preface or introduction. More often than not they are passed over as quickly as possible by the eager reader, anxious to dig for the bounty of the book and too impatient to be instructed on how and where to dig. In the hope of catching the present reader unawares, the guidelines for study are now put forth. Earlier sections of this chapter have introduced the carbonyl compounds, classified them for the ensuing discussion, and illustrated some of the aspects of nomenclature with a few selected examples. The following sections of this chapter discuss the electronic structure, the bond properties, the acid and base properties, and the physicochemical properties of carbonyl compounds. Although familiarity with this material is essential for a complete understanding of the chemistry of carbonyl compounds, much of it can be overlooked at first. It is suggested, therefore, that the student encountering this subject for the first time read quickly through the remainder of this chapter and then pass on to Chap. 2, at which point the chemistry of the carbonyl compounds comes into focus. Chapter 2 should be read with some attention to detail, but without great concern for every fine point, for many of the ideas discussed will become clearer when specific examples are encountered in the two succeeding chapters. Chapters 3 and 4 present examples of the nucleophilic reactions of carbonyl compounds and should be studied in detail. After a thorough perusal of these chapters, it is suggested that the student reread Chap. 2 and consider the several generalizing principles in terms of the many specific examples of Chaps. 3 and 4. Chapters 5 and 6 concern additional aspects of carbonyl reactions and should also be studied in detail. Finally, a rereading of the entire book is suggested. The presentation of a subject such as organic chemistry has no unique starting point and ending point; item A presupposes familiarity with item B, which presupposes familiarity with item C, which presupposes familiarity with item A. As a result of this circularity, one must approach a complete understanding of the subject by a process of repetitive cycling.

1.5 ELECTRONIC BOND STRUCTURE OF
CARBONYL COMPOUNDS

The carbon-oxygen bond in carbonyl compounds is pictured as the overlap of an sp^2 hybrid orbital from carbon and a $2p_x$ orbital from oxygen to form a sigma bond combined with the lateral overlap of the carbon $2p$ orbital and the oxygen $2p_y$ orbital to form a pi bond (see Fig. 1-2).[†] The polarity of the carbon-oxygen "double bond" is thought to reside both in the sigma bond and the pi bond and to be partly responsible for the extra strength as compared with the carbon-carbon "double bond." Whereas the C=C bond strength (146 kcal/mole) is less than twice the C—C bond strength (83 kcal/mole), the C=O bond strength (176–179 kcal/mole) is more than twice the C—O bond strength (85.5 kcal/mole). This is possibly accounted for by the fact that oxygen (unlike carbon) has nonbonded electrons and that the repulsion among these is lower when the oxygen is doubly bonded than when singly bonded. As pictured in Fig. 1-2, the polarity of the carbonyl group requires a molecu-

† For additional details see N. L. Allinger and J. Allinger, *op. cit.*

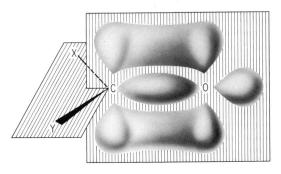

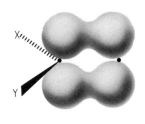

valence bond representation

stylized molecular orbital representation (an additional p orbital and a $2s$ orbital on the oxygen atom are not shown in this representation)

molecular orbital representation of the pi bond

Fig. 1-2 Bonding in carbonyl compounds. (The stylized molecular orbital representation, although less accurate than the right hand representation in depicting the pi bond, will be used, because it more quickly conveys the desired information to the viewer.)

lar orbital representation which shows an increased electron density in the vicinity of the oxygen or a valence bond representation which includes a charge-separated structure.

1.6 STRUCTURE AND PROPERTIES OF
CLASS AA COMPOUNDS

The quintessence of the carbonyl compound is usually taken to be the saturated aliphatic aldehyde or ketone. In these compounds the interaction between the carbonyl group and the attached groups (H or sp^3 hybridized carbon) is usually quite small. As a consequence, the carbonyl group is in the best situation to show its true colors unperturbed by interaction with its neighbors, and compounds of class AA provide a good reference point for discussions of the effects of structure on the properties of carbonyl compounds in general. For instance, the dipole moment of class AA compounds is approximately 2.5 D and is ascribed almost entirely to the dipolar character of the carbon-oxygen double bond; the bond length of class AA compounds is about 1.22 Å and is taken to be that characteristic of the isolated carbonyl group.

The effect of the X and Y groups on the carbonyl function can be discerned by dipole moment and bond length measurements as well as by the interaction of light with carbonyl compounds, i.e. by measurements of infrared spectra, ultraviolet spectra, and refractive indices.[†] For class AA compounds, the most generally useful of these is the infrared spectrum, which shows a strong band (corresponding to the stretching mode of the carbonyl group) at 1705–1740 cm^{-1}, with ketones generally falling near 1715 cm^{-1} and aldehydes near 1730 cm^{-1}. The interactions between the X or Y group and the carbonyl function which tend to shift this absorption may be of an electronic nature or a steric nature. As an example of the former effect, electron-withdrawing groups in X or Y will, in general, shift the absorption to a higher frequency; for instance, acetone absorbs at 1715 cm^{-1}, while α-chloroacetone absorbs at 1724 cm^{-1} and hexafluoroacetone absorbs at 1801 cm^{-1}. Steric influences which result in a change in the C—CO—C bond angle may shift the absorption in either direction. In the family of 4-, 5-, and 6-membered cyclic carbonyl compounds, the frequency of absorption increases as the ring size diminishes and, concomitantly, the C—CO—C bond angle diminishes. Thus, cyclohexanone absorbs at 1715 cm^{-1}, cyclopentanone at 1745 cm^{-1}, and cyclobutanone at 1784 cm^{-1}. Conversely, the steric repulsions in hexamethylacetone increase the C—CO—C bond angle and decrease the frequency of absorption to 1686 cm^{-1}. The relation between the frequency of absorption and the C—CO—C bond angle holds for all classes of carbonyl compounds and is most useful as a method of structure elucidation, particularly in the assignment of ring size for cyclic carbonyl compounds.

1.7 STRUCTURE AND PROPERTIES OF
CLASS AB AND CLASS BB COMPOUNDS

In compounds belonging to class AB and BB, one or both of the attached groups can interact with the carbonyl function not only via the sigma bond (inductive effect) but also via the pi bond (resonance-electromeric effect). The lateral overlap between the C=C pi-bond system and the C=O pi-bond system produces a molecular orbital which encompasses all four atoms as pictured in Fig. 1-3. Such systems are said to be "conjugated." To the extent that this pi-bond delocalization takes place, the carbonyl group loses some of its individual character and shares itself with the olefin group. One consequence of this is a stabilization of the system (delocalization energy 2–3 kcal/mole). Another consequence is a transfer of the electron deficiency from the carbonyl carbon (as in class AA compounds) to the β-carbon atom.

The participation of the carbonyl group in a conjugated system is reflected in its bond properties, which, in turn, affect its spectral properties. The C=O bond distance increases slightly, the refractive index increases

---

† For a detailed discussion of infrared and ultraviolet spectral methods, see J. R. Dyer, *Applications of Absorption Spectroscopy of Organic Compounds* (Englewoods Cliffs, N.J.: Prentice-Hall, Inc., 1965).

appreciably (1.3588 for CH_3COCH_3 to 1.4086 for $CH_3-COCH=CH_2$), and the dipole moment increases significantly (2.57 D for $CH_3CH_2CH_2CHO$ to 3.54 D for $CH_3CH=CH-CHO$). Commensurate with the increase in bond length (indicating less double bond character), the carbonyl stretching frequency in the infrared diminishes by 25–40 cm^{-1}; this provides a useful tool for the detection of α,β-unsaturated structures. The increase in bond length, the increase in dipolar character, and the decrease in the stretching force constant for the carbonyl group in α,β-unsaturated carbonyl compounds are all compatible with

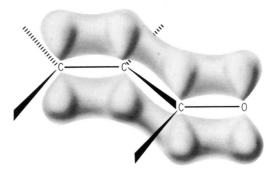

valence bond representation

molecular orbital representation

Fig. 1-3 Structure of α,β-unsaturated aldehydes and ketones.

the notion that, through interaction with the adjacent C=C multiple bond, the carbonyl group has lost some of its double bond character. To the extent that the charge-separated resonance structure shown in Fig. 1-3 contributes to the resonance hybrid, the carbon-oxygen bond acquires single bond character.

Perhaps the most characteristic feature of an α,β-unsaturated carbonyl compound is its ultraviolet absorption spectrum. Although class AA compounds have pi electrons in the C=O bond and $2p$ electrons on the oxygen capable of excitation, the former require light of wavelengths below 200 mμ (a region inaccessible with many spectrophotometers), and the latter have a low excitation probability (a so-called "forbidden transition"). In class AB compounds, however, the electrons associated with the delocalized pi-bond system are excited by wavelengths above 200 mμ, this region being easily attainable with modern spectrophotometers. The occurrence of a strong absorption band above 200 mμ, therefore, is typical of α,β-unsaturated carbonyl compounds and provides a test for the presence of this structural feature. For instance $CH_3CH_2CH_2COCH_3$ is essentially transparent above 200 mμ, but $CH_3CH=CHCOCH_3$ shows an intense absorption at 224 mμ; $C_6H_5CH_2COCH_3$ is transparent above 200 mμ, but $C_6H_5COCH_2CH_3$ has an intense absorption at 244 mμ; formylcyclopentane is transparent above 200 mμ, but 1-formyl-1-cyclopentene has an intense absorption at 237 mμ.

In almost any classification system certain members of a given group show such extreme behavior as to appear to be qualitatively different from the others. In class AA carbonyl compounds, for instance, hexa-fluoroacetone can hardly be taken as a typical member of this group. Similarly, classes AB and BB have abnormal representatives. A good example is the compound cycloheptatrienone (tropone), which is a member of class BB. Its high dipole moment of 4.3 D and its low frequency for the carbonyl stretching absorption at 1638 cm^{-1} indicate that the carbon-oxygen bond has an unusual amount of single bond character. In fact, structure B in Fig. 1-4 is a better representation of tropone than is structure A and quite satisfactorily interprets both the physical and chemical properties of this compound. The importance of structure B arises from the unusually effective manner in which a cyclo-heptatriene ring can delocalize a positive charge (delocalization energy is about 30 kcal/mole).

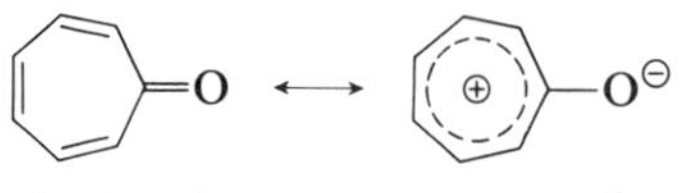

structure A structure B

Fig. 1-4 Resonance structures of cycloheptatrienone (tropone).

1.8 STRUCTURE AND PROPERTIES OF
CLASS AC AND CLASS CC COMPOUNDS

In compounds belonging to class AC and CC the carbonyl group can interact with the attached groups in two ways, i.e., via the sigma bonds and via the pi bonds. Whereas the effect of the carbonyl dipole in class AB and BB compounds is to transmit positive charge to the β-position, in class AC and CC compounds the electron deficiency is transmitted to the attached hetero atom. Thus, in carboxylic acids and carboxylic acid derivatives (the main exemplars of class AC compounds), a delocalized orbital encompasses the carbonyl group and the Y atom, as pictured in Fig. 1-5. In the absence of any pi-bond participation by the Y group, the electron deficiency at the carbonyl carbon is augmented by inductive electron-withdrawal by Y. To the extent that the p electrons of Y participate with the pi orbital of the carbonyl group, however, electron deficiency is transferred from carbonyl carbon to Y. The results of this are profound enough to place the carboxylic acids and their derivatives in a class which is often considered separately from aldehydes and ketones. The magnitude of the departure of RCOY compounds from "true" carbonyl compounds depends upon the Y group and reaches its ultimate in the carboxylate anion, where, as shown in Fig. 1-6, the negative charge is evenly distributed between the two oxygen atoms.

The electron delocalization of class AC and CC compounds stabilizes the molecule to a considerable extent (delocalization energy about 15 kcal/mole). The bond properties of these compounds, however, must be interpreted in terms of the opposing effects of inductive electron withdrawal by the Y group and resonance-electromeric electron release by

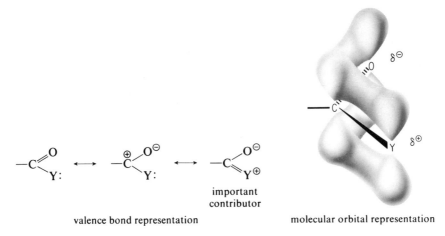

important
contributor

valence bond representation

molecular orbital representation

Fig. 1-5 Structure of carboxylic acids and derivatives.

the Y group. In the case of acid chlorides $\left(RC\begin{smallmatrix}O\\Cl\end{smallmatrix}\right)$, the former is more important, as indicated by the shortened C=O bond length (1.17 Å) and the increased frequency of infrared absorption (1770–1815 cm^{-1}). In the case of esters $\left(RC\begin{smallmatrix}O\\OR'\end{smallmatrix}\right)$, the effects approximately cancel each other, and the bond lengths (1.22 Å) and stretching frequencies (1735–1750 cm^{-1}) are comparable with those in class AA compounds. In the case of the

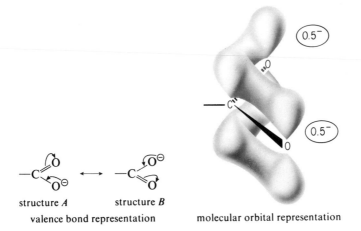

structure *A*   structure *B*

valence bond representation

molecular orbital representation

Fig. 1-6 Structure of the carboxylate anion.

carboxylate ion $\left(RC \underset{O}{\overset{O}{\diagdown}} \ominus \right)$, the resonance-electromeric electron contribution is the more important effect, as indicated by the increased bond length (1.31 Å) and the decreased frequency of infrared absorption (1550–1600 cm^{-1}). To the extent that the Y group releases electrons to the carbonyl carbon, the electron deficiency of the latter is diminished, and phenomena depending upon this deficiency are depressed. Thus, acid chlorides are more carbonyl-like than carboxylate anions in many of the chemical reactions discussed in later chapters.

1.9 STRUCTURE AND PROPERTIES OF
CLASS BC COMPOUNDS

In compounds belonging to class BC, both of the attached groups can interact with the pi bond of the carbonyl group *but* in competing fashions. One group diminishes the positive charge on the carbonyl carbon by contribution of electron density from an olefinic pi bond (to establish the positive charge on the β-carbon), while the other group achieves the same result by contribution of electron density from nonbonded p electrons (to establish the positive charge on the hetero atom). Valence bond and molecular orbital representations for this class of compounds are illustrated in Fig. 1-7.

Since both of the attached groups participate with the carbonyl pi bond in class BC compounds, it might be predicted that neither involvement would be individually as effective as it would be in the absence of the other group (e.g., class BC compared with class AB; class BC compared with class AC). For instance, the introduction of α,β-olefinic unsaturation into an aldehyde or ketone (class AA → class AB) reduces the carbonyl stretching frequency by about 40 cm^{-1}, but this same structural change in a saturated carboxylic acid or derivative (class AC → class BC) causes only a 20 cm^{-1} reduction in stretching frequency. Similarly, the difference in dipole moment between class AA and AB compounds is greater than the difference between class AC and BC compounds, indicating that the degree to which the positive charge is localized on the β-carbon atom is diminished in class BC compounds as compared with class AB compounds.

1.10 STRUCTURE AND PROPERTIES OF
CLASS D COMPOUNDS

Class D compounds require an electronic description different from that which suffices for all of the other carbonyl compounds. In this case it is necessary to ascribe sp hybridization to the carbonyl carbon to allow it to engage in two sigma-pi double bondings as illustrated in Fig. 1-8.

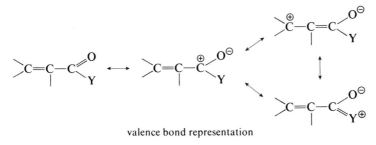

valence bond representation

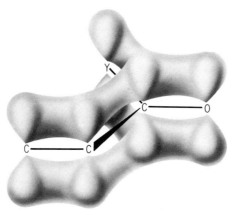

molecular orbital representation

Fig. 1-7 Structure of α,β-unsaturated carboxylic acid derivatives.

Since the hybridization of the carbon in class D compounds is the same as that in carbon monoxide and different from that of the carbonyl compounds in class AA through class CC, it is not surprising to find the bond properties of class D compounds tending in the direction of carbon monoxide. The carbon-oxygen bond lengths of ketene (1.15 Å) and

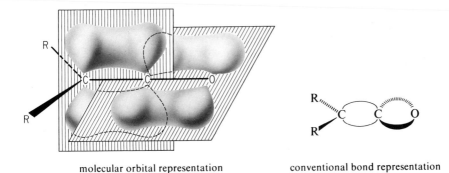

molecular orbital representation   conventional bond representation

Fig. 1-8 Structure of ketenes.

methyl isocyanate (1.18 Å) are fairly close to that of carbon monoxide (1.13 Å); the stretching frequencies of ketenes (2150 cm^{-1}) and isocyanates (2270 cm^{-1}) are comparable with that of carbon monoxide (2143 cm^{-1}).

1.11 TAUTOMERISM IN CARBONYL COMPOUNDS

The infrared spectrum of ethyl α,α-dimethylacetoacetate (see Fig. 1-9) is normal and possesses a band at 1718 cm^{-1} (characteristic of a saturated

ethyl α,α-dimethylacetoacetate
($\tilde{\nu}_{cm^{-1}}$ 1718, 1742)

ethyl acetoacetate (acetoacetic ester)
($\tilde{\nu}_{cm^{-1}}$ 1650, 1718, 1742)

3,3-dimethylpentane-2,4-dione
($\tilde{\nu}_{cm^{-1}}$ 1715)

pentane-2,4-dione
($\tilde{\nu}_{cm^{-1}}$ 1540–1640)

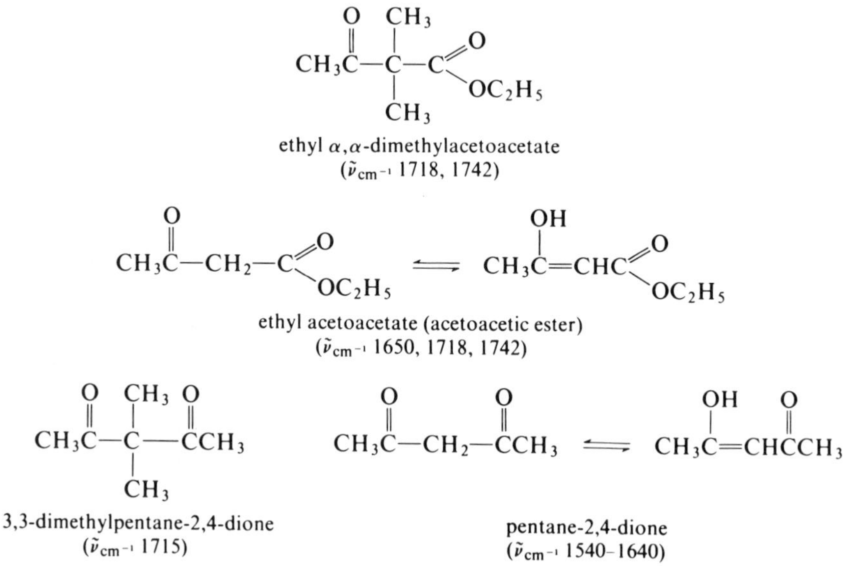

Fig. 1-9 Structure and carbonyl stretching frequencies of β-dicarbonyl compounds.

ketone) and a band at 1742 cm^{-1} (characteristic of a saturated ester). The infrared spectrum of the unmethylated analog, ethyl acetoacetate (aceto-acetic ester), however, contains a third band at 1650 cm^{-1} (characteristic of an α,β-unsaturated carbonyl compound). Similarly, 3,3-dimethyl-pentane-2,4-dione possesses a normal carbonyl stretching band at 1715 cm^{-1}, while the unmethylated analog pentane-2,4-dione lacks this band completely and instead shows a very strong and broad band at 1540–1640 cm^{-1}. In both cases the placement of a hydrogen atom on the carbon between the two carbonyl groups appears to alter the spectral characteristics of the carbonyl group in a significant way. That this feature alters the chemical characteristics of β-dicarbonyl compounds as well was realized decades ago, and this fact instigated one of the classical contro-versies of organic chemistry, namely, deciding upon the structure of acetoacetic ester. Many reactions of acetoacetic ester indicate that it con-

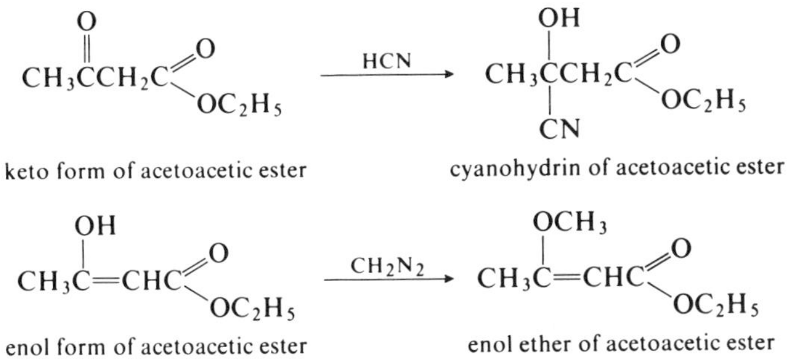

Fig. 1-10 Keto and enol forms of acetoacetic ester.

tains an ordinary carbonyl group (e.g., cyanohydrin formation as illustrated in Fig. 1-10). However, it also manifests behavior characteristic of phenols: it is measurably acidic, forms a sodium salt, gives a color with ferric chloride, and reacts with diazomethane to give an ether (see Fig. 1-10). This schizoid behavior was baffling to the organic chemists of the nineteenth century, and it was not until the notion could be accepted that acetoacetic ester is actually a mixture of compounds that the dilemma was resolved. It is now realized that acetoacetic ester under ordinary conditions is comprised of two compounds, designated as the keto and enol forms, which can be separated and maintained as individual entities only by special means.[†] Except in the complete absence of acidic or basic catalysts, the keto and enol forms are rapidly interconvertible and exist in a mobile equilibrium, the position of which for a given compound is determined by the solvent, the concentration, and the temperature.[‡]

As already mentioned, every class has its eccentrics which, for one reason or another, exhibit behavior different from that of the other members of the class. The eccentrics of the β-dicarbonyl compounds are structures in which the carbon atom between the carbonyl groups is at a bridgehead position of a bicyclic system. Bicyclo[2.2.1]heptan-2,6-dione (see Fig. 1-11), for instance, shows properties of a simple ketone and has no tendency whatsoever to enolize in the direction of the bridgehead carbon. The explanation of this behavior is to be found in the greatly increased strain that would be introduced into the molecule if an enol

[†] Crystallization of acetoacetic ester from certain organic solvents at low temperatures (about $-80°C$) gives the pure keto form of acetoacetic ester. Careful treatment of a petroleum ether suspension of the sodium enolate with hydrogen chloride at this low temperature gives the pure enol form. In quartz vessels and in the absence of acid or base, the keto and enol forms may be kept for relatively long periods of time without reversion to the equilibrium mixture.

[‡] In pure acetoacetic ester in the condensed phase, the enol content is approximately 8%, whereas in the vapor phase it is about 50%; in dilute aqueous solution the enol content is 0.4%, while in hexane solution it is 46%.

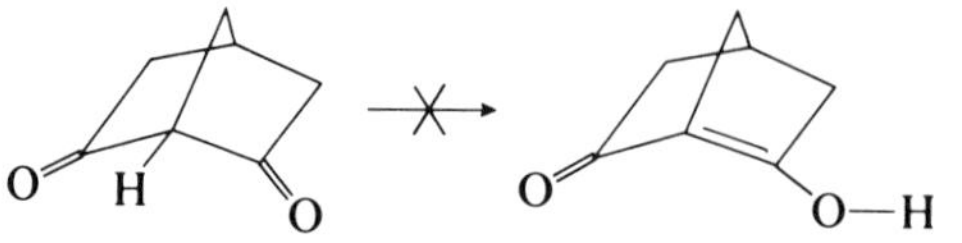

Fig. 1-11 Non-enolizability of bicyclo[2.2.1] heptan-2,6-dione.

structure were to exist. The favorable energy considerations responsible for an ordinary β-dicarbonyl compound seeking to equilibrate with the enol form are more than counterbalanced by the very unfavorable energy requirements of placing a double bond at the bridgehead of a bicyclic system.[†]

The tendency for β-dicarbonyl compounds to equilibrate with the enol form represents a quantitative, but not a qualitative, difference from simple carbonyl compounds. Simple carbonyl compounds having at least one hydrogen attached to the carbon adjacent to the carbonyl group can also exist in equilibrium with an enol form, although in the majority of cases the concentration of enol is so small that it can be disregarded so far as structural representations are concerned. It may, however, be an important factor in the chemical behavior of the molecule, for certain reactions proceed by way of the enol form.

If bicyclo[2.2.1]heptan-2,6-dione is taken as an eccentric of the non-enolizable right, then phenols must be taken as examples of eccentrics on the ultra-enolizable left. The incorporation of a carbonyl group into a cyclohexadienone structure produces a compound which has an overwhelming compulsion to become enolic. The energy factors favoring the keto form are more than counterbalanced by the favorable energy factors in the enol which allow aromatic stabilization. Thus, the keto-enol equilibrium of cyclohexadienone is so favorable to the enol form (see Fig. 1-12) that the proper formulation of the structure is as the phenol. This class of compounds will not be included as examples of carbonyl compounds.

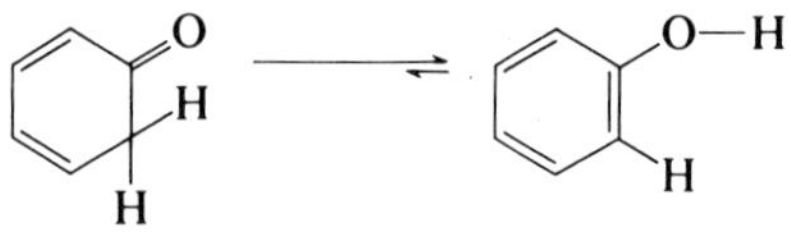

Fig. 1-12 Keto-enol equilibrium of cyclohexadienone.

In general, the boiling point of an alcohol is greater than that of the corresponding ketone, and the solubility of an alcohol in an inert solvent such as hexane is less than that of the corresponding ketone. These relationships are reversed in the case of the keto and enol forms of acetoacetic ester, however. Also significant is the stretching absorption of the O—H group, which in simple alcohols and phenols is ordinarily observed in the infrared region around 3500 cm^{-1}, but is shifted to considerably lower frequencies in acetoacetic ester. All of these observations are interpretable

---

† The failure of bicyclo[2.2.1]heptan-2,6-dione to enolize is an example of the operation of Bredt's rule, which is an empirically-derived statement regarding the ease with which a double bond can be accommodated at a bridgehead position in a bridged ring structure. Compounds in which the number of bridging atoms is less than 8 (the number is 5 in the bicyclo [2.2.1] heptane system) "obey" Bredt's rule and fail to enolize.

in terms of an intramolecularly hydrogen-bonded structure for the enol form, as depicted in Fig. 1-13. In ordinary alcohols, the high boiling points, the low hexane solubility, and the appearance of an O—H stretching band near 3500 cm^{-1} are all dependent on a free OH group. The incorporation of the OH into a quasi six-membered ring through intramolecular hydrogen bonding alters the usual polar and bond characteristics in a striking way and produces a type of compound known as a chelate structure.

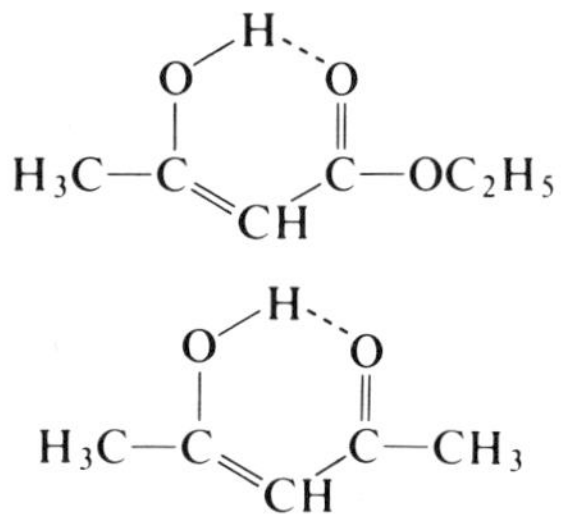

Fig. 1-13 Chelated enol structures of ethyl acetoacetate and pentan-2,4-dione.

1.12 ACID AND BASE PROPERTIES OF CARBONYL COMPOUNDS

The electronic structures of carbonyl compounds have been discussed in relation to various bond properties for unperturbed molecules. Of more significance to the chemist interested in chemical behavior is the relation between the electronic structure of a compound and its sensitivity to the perturbing influences of other chemical species. As a prelude for studying the chemistry of carbonyl compounds, the following sections will be concerned with the ability of these compounds to accept or donate electrons and protons; such information provides a good index of their chemical reactivity.

The carbonyl group as an electron donor (Lewis base): In addition to the electrons of the carbon-oxygen double bond, the oxygen atom of a carbonyl group carries four nonbonding electrons in its outer valence shell. As a consequence of these, and as a consequence of the greater electronegativity of oxygen relative to carbon (carbon is 2.5 and oxygen is 3.5 on the Pauling scale), the oxygen atom is electron-rich compared to the carbon atom. This is manifested by a permanent dipole moment and by electron-donating propensities, i.e., the carbonyl group acts as a basic center (a Lewis base), also designated as a nucleophilic center. As acceptor for the electrons provided by the carbonyl oxygen, any electron deficient species will suffice (i.e., cations as well as Lewis acids). Among the most powerful of these are protons and various metal salts, such as aluminum chloride, boron trifluoride, and stannic chloride.

For a given carbonyl compound, the extent to which a proton can be transferred to it depends upon the strength of the acid that is used. Acetone, for instance, is almost completely protonated by concentrated sulfuric acid and is half protonated by 82% sulfuric acid. For a given acid, the extent of carbonyl protonation depends upon the particular carbonyl compound. Thus, under conditions where benzaldehyde is half protonated (by 82% sulfuric acid), acetophenone is nine tenths protonated. The greater basicity of the carbonyl oxygen of acetophenone is attributed to the electron-releasing ability of a methyl group as compared with hydrogen. Although measurably basic, carbonyl compounds are very weak in comparison with compounds more generally classed as bases. Acetophenone, for instance, is almost 10^{12} times less basic than aniline and 10^{17} times less basic than aliphatic amines. Even in this region of low basicity, however, substituent effects are manifested and can be measured quantitatively. For instance, the electron-withdrawing nitro group in the p-position reduces the basicity of acetophenone fifty-fold, while the electron-releasing methoxyl group in the p-position increases the basicity twenty-fivefold.[†]

Carbonyl compounds can react with cations (of which the proton is a specific example) and also with certain neutral but electron deficient species. Aluminum chloride, for instance, forms complexes (see Fig. 1-14) which may sometimes be isolated. Frequently, however, the induced dis-

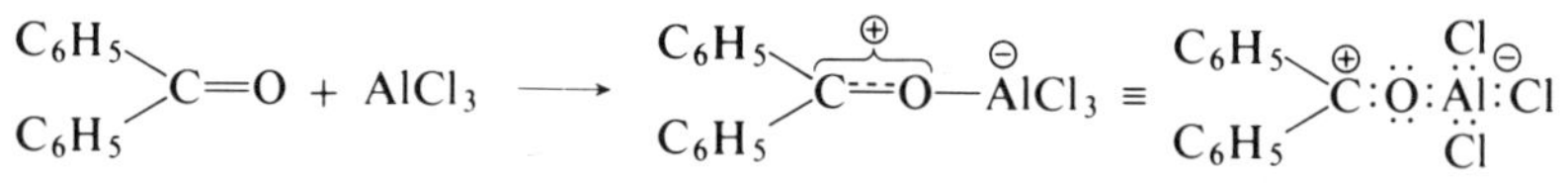

Fig. 1-14 Aluminum chloride complex of benzophenone.

tortion of the electrons of the carbonyl group promotes chemical reactions, and for this reason aluminum chloride and other Lewis acids are often employed, as is the proton, as reaction catalysts.

The carbonyl group as an electron acceptor (Lewis acid): The fact that carbonyl groups can accept electrons is attested by the numerous reactions in which atoms or groups are added across the carbon-oxygen double bond (see Chap. 2). Instead of an atom or group, it is also possible to add just an electron to give a species described as a radical anion (see Fig. 1-15). This may be accomplished by means of certain strongly elec-

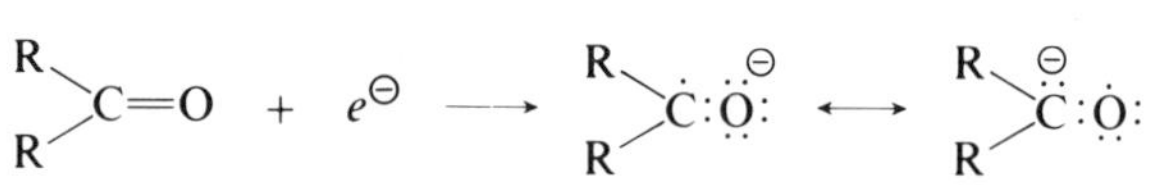

Fig. 1-15 Radical anions from carbonyl compounds.

tropositive metals, such as sodium, or by electrical discharge at an electrode. Radical anions are generally unstable; although they can be detected and studied under certain conditions, they tend to acquire another electron (with or without an attached group) to form various products.

---

† For a detailed discussion of the effects of substituent groups on chemical behavior see R. Stewart, *The Investigation of Organic Reactions* (Englewood Cliffs, N.J.: Prentice-Hall, Inc., 1966).

Carbonyl compounds as proton donors: The ability of the carbonyl group to accept electrons imputes to it the characteristics of an acid in the Lewis sense. While the carbonyl group per se can act as an acid *only* in this sense, carbonyl compounds containing a hydrogen atom attached to the atom α to the carbonyl group may function as *proton acids* as well. The lability of the H—Y bond in structures of the type H—Y—C=O, as illustrated in Fig. 1-16, is ascribed to the capacity of the carbonyl group for orbital overlap with the free or developing (as the H departs) p orbital on the Y group. To the extent that a charge or an electron can be de-

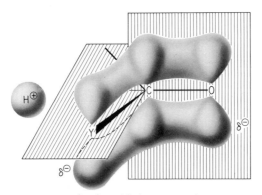

valence bond representation

molecular orbital representation

Fig. 1-16 Carbonyl compounds as proton donors.

localized over the three-atom system Y—C—O, the cleavage of the H—Y bond is facilitated by stabilization of the resulting cleavage product. In the case most usual for carbonyl compounds, the cleavage is heterolytic and leads to a proton and an anion, i.e., the carbonyl compound behaves as a proton acid.

The acidity of compounds of structure H—Y—C=O is strongly influenced by the identity of the atom Y and increases as Y progresses from carbon to nitrogen to oxygen. Thus, $RCOCH_3$ has a pK_A of 19, $RCONH_2$ has a pK_A of 15, and RCO_2H has a pK_A of 5. Carboxylic acids, compounds of the structure RCO_2H, are in fact so very much more acidic than their carbon atom or nitrogen atom counterparts that they are usually treated as a separate class of carbonyl compounds. They are acidic enough to taste sour, to turn blue litmus paper red, to produce conducting solutions when dissolved in water, and to be titratable with moderately strong bases. Any difference from their carbon atom and nitrogen atom counterparts, however, is only a quantitative one; the interpretation of the acidities is the same in all three cases.

While monocarbonyl compounds such as CH_3COCH_3, $CH_3CO_2C_2H_5$, etc. are very weakly acidic (pK_A 19), β-dicarbonyl compounds such as $CH_3COCH_2COCH_3$ (pK_A 9.0) and $CH_3COCH_2CO_2C_2H_5$ (pK_A 10.7) are several orders of magnitude more acidic. That even simple carbonyl compounds have the capability of dissociating a hydrogen, however, is indicated by the base-induced deuterium-hydrogen exchange; for example, CH_3COCH_3 treated with D_2O and NaOD gives CD_3COCD_3. The greater acidity of acetone (pK_A 19) as compared with methane (pK_A about 40) may be partly ascribed to the inductive electron withdrawing power of the carbonyl group. But this alone is an insufficient explanation, as indicated by the fact that ketone A in Fig. 1-17 readily exchanges its two α-hydrogens for deuterium in the presence of alkaline D_2O, whereas ketone B in Fig. 1-17 fails to undergo any significant exchange. The polarities of

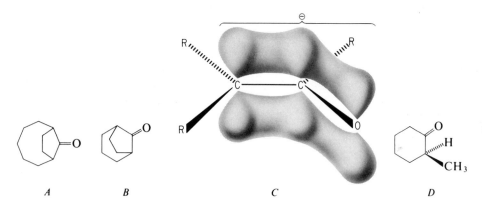

A   *B*   *C*   *D*

Fig. 1-17   Delocalization in α-carbonyl carbanions (enolate anions).

the carbonyl group in the two molecules must be virtually identical, the only difference between the two systems being the ease with which twisting in the vicinity of the α-carbon can take place. The geometry of ketone A allows the necessary distortion for carbanion stabilization via delocalization, while the geometry of ketone B does not (recall Bredt's rule, p. 14). These data indicate that hydrogen atoms attached to the α-position of carbonyl compounds are significantly acidic only if there can be charge delocalization from the carbon to the oxygen. This, in turn, demands that the α-carbon be sp^2 hybridized and that the p orbitals on the α-carbon, the carbonyl carbon, and the oxygen become collinear, i.e., that the geometry of the α-carbanion become planar (structure C in Fig. 1-17). In accordance with this concept, optically active compounds such as ($+$)

2-methylcyclohexanone (structure *D* in Fig. 1-17) are racemized when treated with basic reagents.

While the stability of anions derived from class AA and AC carbonyl compounds is ascribed to electron delocalization over the three atom system $[Y\text{-----}C\text{-----}O]^{\ominus}$, in class AB, BB, and BC compounds the delocalized system can extend over a greater number of atomic centers. For example, the anion derived from crotonaldehyde (see Fig. 1-18) possesses a high

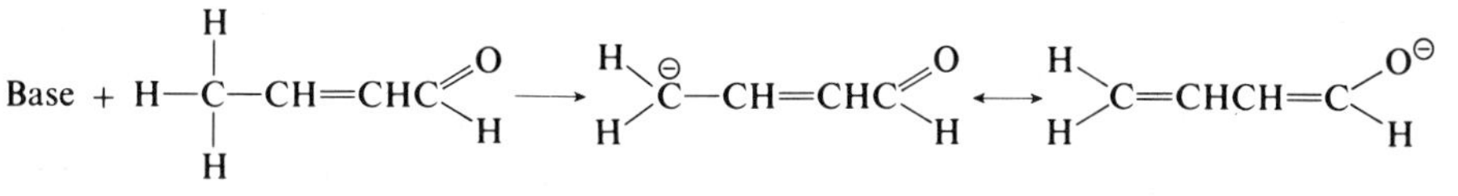

Fig. 1-18   Lability of the γ-proton in crotonaldehyde.

electron density at the γ-carbon atom and involves delocalization over five centers. Systems of the general structure $Z\text{---}Y(\overset{|}{C}\text{=}\overset{|}{C})_n\overset{|}{C}\text{=}O$ qualitatively resemble the simple system $Z\text{---}Y\text{---}C\text{=}O$ with respect to the labilizing effect of the carbonyl group on the $Z\text{---}Y$ bond. This phenomenon is an example of the transmission of electrical effects through conjugated systems and, in structures of the type represented by class AB, BB, and BC carbonyl compounds, has been referred to as the *principle of vinylogy*. Compounds related to each other as crotonaldehyde is related to acetaldehyde are said to be vinylogs.

1.13 CONCLUSION

Carbonyl compounds have been treated in this chapter as a single class whose representatives vary, with respect to electronic bond structure, spectral characteristics, and acid-base properties, as the groups attached to the carbonyl function vary. The "carbonyl character" is generally greatest for class AA compounds and diminishes in the progression AA > AB > AC > BC > CC. Some of the chemical characteristics of class AA compounds (simple aldehydes and ketones), class AB and BB compounds (α,β-unsaturated aldehydes and ketones, aromatic aldehydes, and ketones), and class AC, BC, and CC compounds (carboxylic acids and derivatives) appear to be sufficiently disparate that these classes are often treated as qualitatively different species. Most of the differences are quantitative rather than qualitative, however, and in later chapters the discussion of the chemical reactions of these compounds will reveal many similarities. For this reason, carbonyl compounds will continue to be treated in this book as a single class in which ketones, aldehydes, carboxylic acids, etc. are but representative members with certain specialized characteristics.

PROBLEMS

Nomenclature

Although not discussed in this book, nomenclature of organic compounds is an important aspect of organic chemistry. Unfortunately, the learning of nomenclature is frequently avoided by the student because of the complications and exasperations that it entails. The complications arise because a definitive name is often cumbersome; the exasperations arise because the same compound often parades under several names, some trivial and some systematic. These facts are not to be legislated out of existence, however, so it is necessary to learn to live with them. The following questions are designed to introduce the student to the realities of nomenclature which are encountered when the organic chemist endeavors to purchase chemicals from a chemical supply house. For these and later questions in this book the student is urged to acquire a catalog from one or more of the following companies:

> Aldrich Chemical Company, Inc.
> 2371 North 30th St.
> Milwaukee, Wisconsin 53210

> Distillation Products Industries
> Eastman Organic Chemicals Department
> Rochester 3, New York

> Matheson Coleman and Bell
> Post Office Box 85
> East Rutherford, New Jersey

1. What are the names used by the catalogs for the first five members in the homologous series of aliphatic aldehydes, ketones, and carboxylic acids? Include all of the possible straight chain and branched chain isomers.

2. Which of the branched chain members of the aliphatic aldehydes, ketones, and carboxylic acids containing from three to six carbon atoms can be purchased for less than $10 per 100 g.

3. Which carboxylic acid derivatives (including acid chlorides, acid anhydrides, ethyl esters, and amides) are available for the first six members of the aliphatic homologous series?

4. Classify each of the compounds in the two columns below by the system described in Sec. 1.2 of this chapter. Indicate which of them can be purchased from chemical supply houses for less than $10 per 100 g.

a. $CH_3(CH_2)_5CHO$

b. $C_6H_5CH_2CHO$

c. $CH_3CH_2CH_2CH_2CHCHO$
$|$
C_2H_5

d. 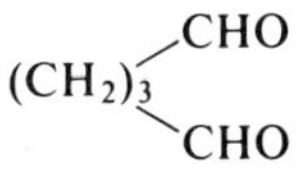 $(CH_2)_3$
$\begin{array}{c} CHO \\ CHO \end{array}$

q.

e. $CH_3(CH_2)_{16}CO_2H$

f. $C_6H_5CH_2CO_2H$

g. Cl_3CCO_2H

h. $CH_3OCH_2CO_2H$

i. 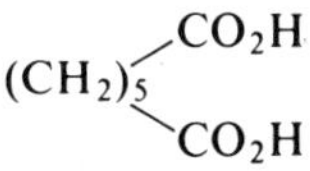 $(CH_2)_5$
$\begin{array}{c} CO_2H \\ CO_2H \end{array}$

j. $\underset{\underset{Cl}{|}}{CH_3CHCOCl}$

k.

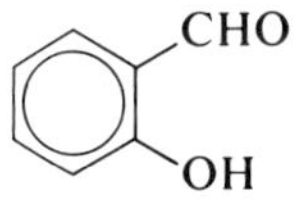

l.

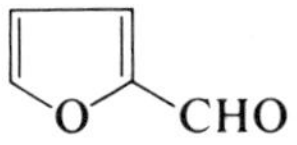

m.

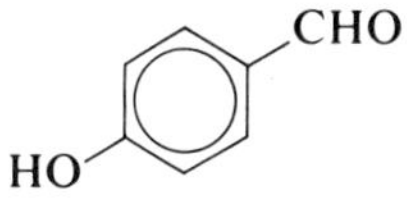

n.

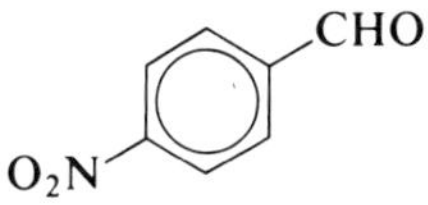

o.

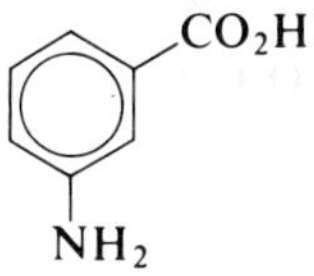

p.

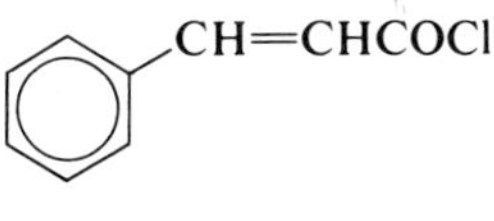

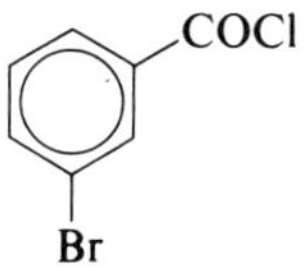

r.

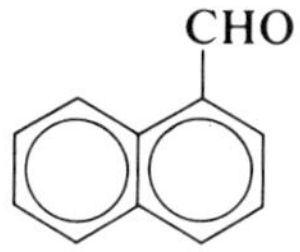

s.

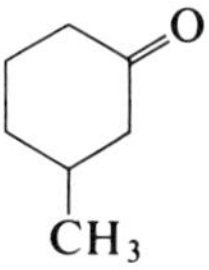

t.

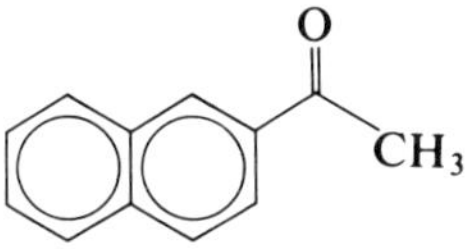

u. $C_6H_5CH_2COCH_3$

v. $C_6H_5COCH_2CH_3$

w. $HCO_2CH_2CH_2CH_3$

x. $CH_3CO_2C_6H_5$

y. $BrCH_2CO_2C_2H_5$

z. $CH_3CO_2CH_2CH{=}CH_2$

aa. $\underset{\underset{CH_2CO_2CH_2C_6H_5}{|}}{CH_2CO_2CH_2C_6H_5}$

bb.

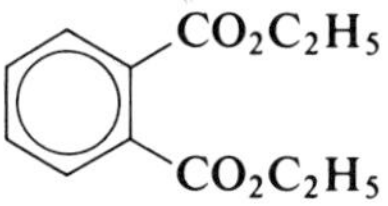

Structure and Properties

1. Write valence bond structures, molecular orbital pictures, and tautomeric structures for the following compounds: $CH_3COCH_2CO_2C_2H_5$, $CH_3CO_2C_2H_5$, $CH_3CH=CHCOCH_3$, CH_3CONH_2, cyclohexadienone,

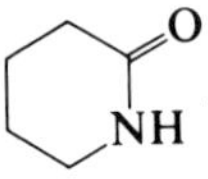

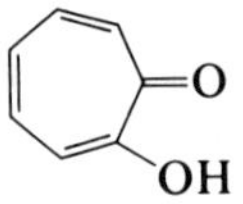

2. For each of the following groups of compounds indicate how, by means of infrared and/or ultraviolet spectral measurements, a differentiation among the members of the group could be made.

a.

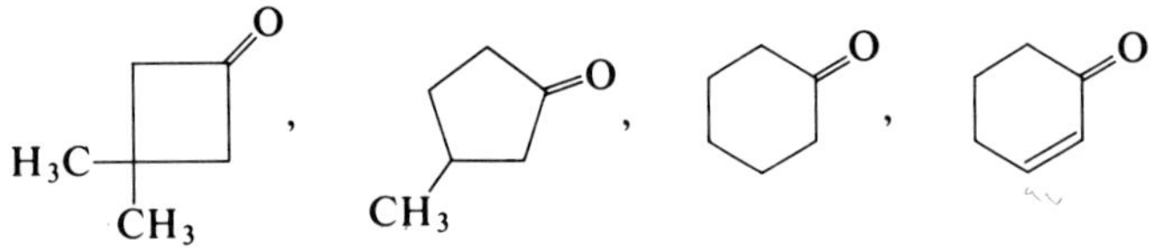

b.

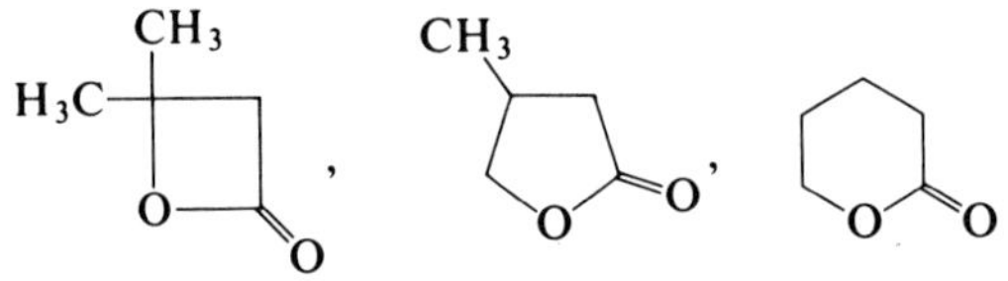

c. $RCOCl$, $RCO_2C_2H_5$, $RCO_2^{\ominus}NH_4^{\oplus}$

d. $(CH_3)_2C=CHCOCH_3$,

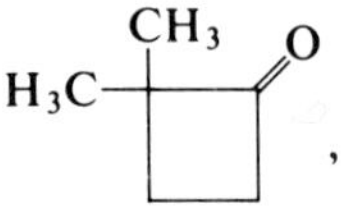

$(CH_3)_2CHCH_2COCH_3$, $(CH_3)_2C=CHCO_2CH_3$, $(CH_3)_3CCHO$

e.

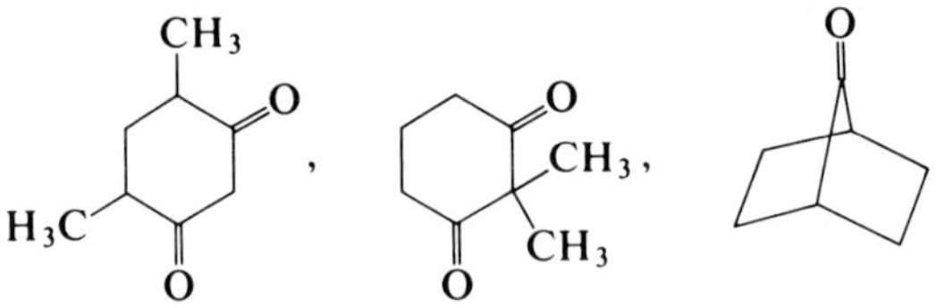

3. Arrange the compounds CH_3COCH_3, $CH_3CH=CHCOCH_3$, $CH_3CO_2C_2H_5$, CH_3CONH_2, and $CH_3CH=CHCO_2C_2H_5$ in order of:

     a. Increasing "carbonyl properties"

     b. Increasing carbonyl stretching force constants

     c. Increasing dipole moments

4. Explain, by the use of resonance structures, the following observations:

a. CH_3O—⟨benzene⟩—$COCH_3$ has a more basic carbonyl group than

O_2N—⟨benzene⟩—$COCH_3$

b. CH_3CHO is more acidic than C_2H_6

c. CH_3CONH_2 is more acidic than CH_3COCH_3

d. ⟨cyclopentylidene⟩$=O$ is more acidic than ⟨bicyclic ketone⟩

e. $(C_2H_5)_2NCOC_2H_5$ is less basic than ⟨bicyclic N-containing ketone⟩

f. $CH_3\overset{O}{\overset{\|}{C}}CH=\underset{OH}{\overset{|}{C}}CH_3$ is a stronger base than $CH_3\overset{O}{\overset{\|}{C}}C=CH_2$ with OH

g. The radical anion from benzophenone is more stable than the radical anion from cyclohexanone.

SELECTED REFERENCES

Detailed discussions of nomenclature are to be found in (a) *Handbook for Chemical Society Authors*, London: The Chemical Society, 1960; (b) A. M. Patterson, L. T. Capell, and D. F. Walker, *The Ring Index*, American Chemical Society Publication, 1960. Detailed discussions of certain of the topics covered in this chapter are to be found in (a) G. W. Wheland, *Advanced Organic Chemistry* (3rd ed.), New York: John Wiley & Sons, Inc., 1960. See Chap. 14, Tautomerism; (b) E. M. Arnett, "Quantitative Comparisons of Weak Organic Bases," *Progress in Physical Organic Chemistry*, Vol. 1, New York: Interscience Publishers, Inc., 1963, p. 223; (c) G. C. Pimentel and A. L. McClellan, *The Hydrogen Bond*, New York: Reinhold Publishing Corp., 1960.

2

Mechanisms
of Nucleophilic Addition
and Addition-Elimination
Reactions
of Carbonyl Compounds

2.1 INTRODUCTION

Having discussed carbonyl compounds in terms of electronic bond properties, spectral characteristics, and acid-base properties in Chap. 1, attention is now directed to their chemical behavior. Chapter 2 will stress the general mechanisms that are thought to be involved in nucleophilic addition and addition-elimination reactions, and Chaps. 3 and 4 will then outline the wide variety of reactions which fall in this class. At this point, the advice given in Sec. 1.4 is reiterated, namely, that Chap. 2 should be read rather quickly the first time through and then reread more carefully after Chaps. 3 and 4 have been digested.

Many of the reactions of carbonyl compounds occur in such a fashion that the partner with which the carbonyl compound is reacting (a nucleophilic reagent) supplies electrons to an electron-deficient center of the carbonyl system. Such reactions are classed as *nucleophilic displacements* in the sense that the direction of electron movement is away from the incoming nucleophilic reagent and toward the oxygen atom of the carbonyl group.[†] Since the bond being displaced, however, is part of a double bond system (i.e., the C=O bond), both the oxygen atom and the incoming nucleophile are retained in the product. As a consequence, these reactions are more commonly designated as *nucleophilic additions* and can be divided into three major groups: (a) direct carbonyl addition; (b) indirect or conjugate carbonyl addition; (c) carbonyl addition-elimination.

[†] For a discussion of nucleophilic displacement reactions at saturated centers, see W. H. Saunders, Jr., *Ionic Aliphatic Reactions* (Englewood Cliffs, N.J.: Prentice-Hall, Inc., 1965).

For instance, cyanide ion is a nucleophilic reagent which can add in the direct sense to most aldehydes and some ketones, can add in the indirect or conjugate sense to many α,β-unsaturated carbonyl compounds, and which can engage in addition-elimination with acid chlorides as illustrated by the examples in Fig. 2-1. The mechanisms of these types of reactions will now be discussed.

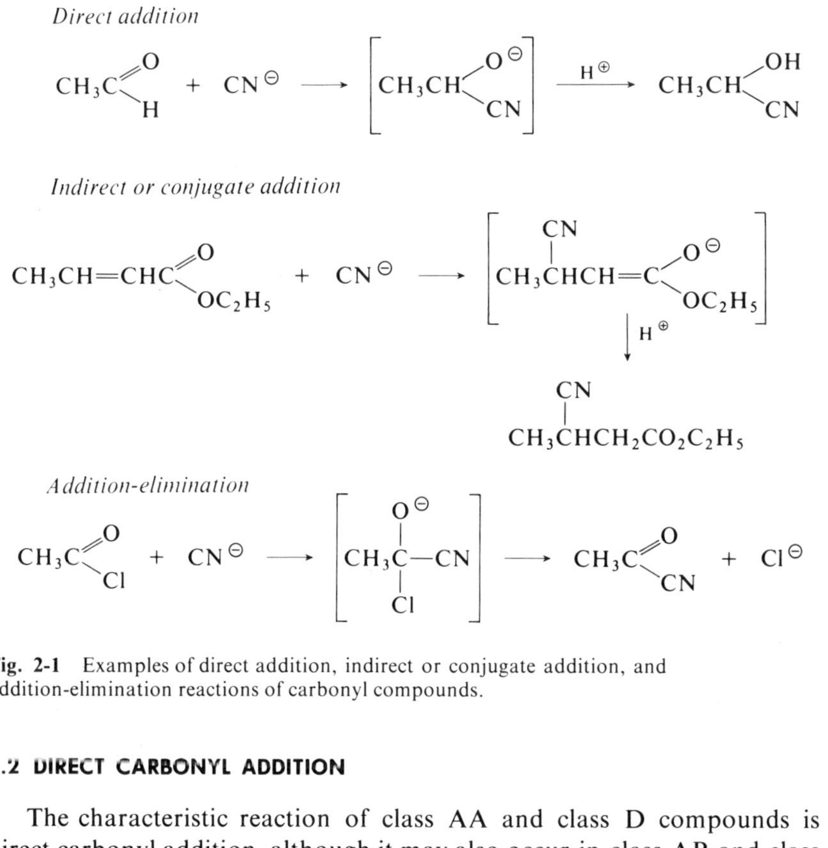

Direct addition

$$CH_3C\overset{O}{\underset{H}{\diagdown}} \ + \ CN^{\ominus} \ \longrightarrow \ \left[CH_3CH\overset{O^{\ominus}}{\underset{CN}{\diagup}} \right] \ \overset{H^{\oplus}}{\longrightarrow} \ CH_3CH\overset{OH}{\underset{CN}{\diagup}}$$

Indirect or conjugate addition

$$CH_3CH{=}CHC\overset{O}{\underset{OC_2H_5}{\diagdown}} \ + \ CN^{\ominus} \ \longrightarrow \ \left[\underset{CH_3CHCH=C}{\overset{CN}{|}}\overset{O^{\ominus}}{\underset{OC_2H_5}{\diagup}} \right] \Bigg\downarrow H^{\oplus}$$

$$\underset{CH_3CHCH_2CO_2C_2H_5}{\overset{\overset{CN}{|}}{}}$$

Addition-elimination

$$CH_3C\overset{O}{\underset{Cl}{\diagdown}} \ + \ CN^{\ominus} \ \longrightarrow \ \left[\underset{Cl}{\overset{\overset{O^{\ominus}}{|}}{CH_3C-CN}} \right] \ \longrightarrow \ CH_3C\overset{O}{\underset{CN}{\diagdown}} \ + \ Cl^{\ominus}$$

Fig. 2-1 Examples of direct addition, indirect or conjugate addition, and addition-elimination reactions of carbonyl compounds.

2.2 DIRECT CARBONYL ADDITION

The characteristic reaction of class AA and class D compounds is direct carbonyl addition, although it may also occur in class AB and class BB compounds. The reaction involves the attack of a nucleophilic species (either a Lewis base or an anion) at the carbonyl carbon to give an intermediate in which the electron density at oxygen has increased. An electrophilic species (Lewis acid or proton) is also involved at some stage of the process; in acid-catalyzed additions the electrophilic species is associated with the oxygen *before* the nucleophilic attack, whereas in the base-catalyzed additions it tags along *after* the nucleophilic attack. A general formulation for these sequences is shown in Fig. 2-2. In this and later figures, base species will be indicated as B (e.g., Me_3N), as $B^{\ominus}$ (e.g., $HO^{\ominus}$, $CH_3O^{\ominus}$, $NH_2^{\ominus}$), or as BH (e.g., HOH, CH_3OH, NH_3); acid species will

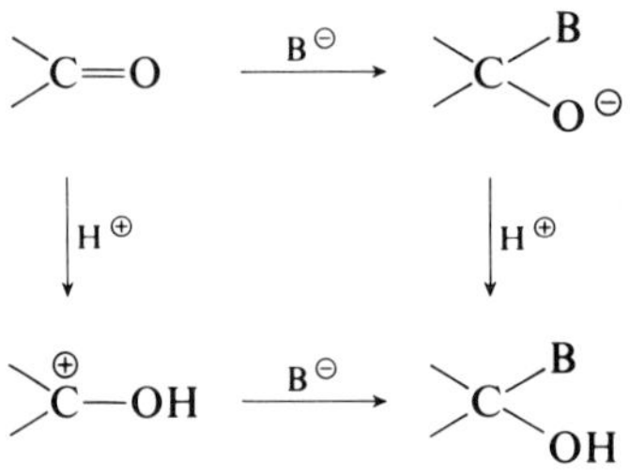

Fig. 2-2 Nucleophilic addition reactions.

be indicated in the cationic form as the proton, $H^{\oplus}$, or in the neutral form as HA (e.g., HCl, $HOCOCH_3$, HOC_6H_5). Keep in mind, however, that BH and HA are qualitatively similar species in that both are dissociable to $H^{\oplus}$ and the conjugate base, $B^{\ominus}$ or $A^{\ominus}$.

An example of a carbonyl addition reaction that can be catalyzed either by acids or by bases is the hydration of aldehydes and ketones. The addition of water to acetaldehyde, for instance, has been shown to be very slow at pH 7 but to proceed much more rapidly at pH 4 and pH 11. In the acid-catalyzed reaction the rate-determining step is the attack of a neutral water molecule (nucleophilic species) on a protonated carbonyl species as represented in Fig. 2-3. In the base-catalyzed reaction, on the other hand, the rate-determining step is the attack of hydroxide ion (nucleophilic species) on the free carbonyl group as illustrated in Fig. 2-4.

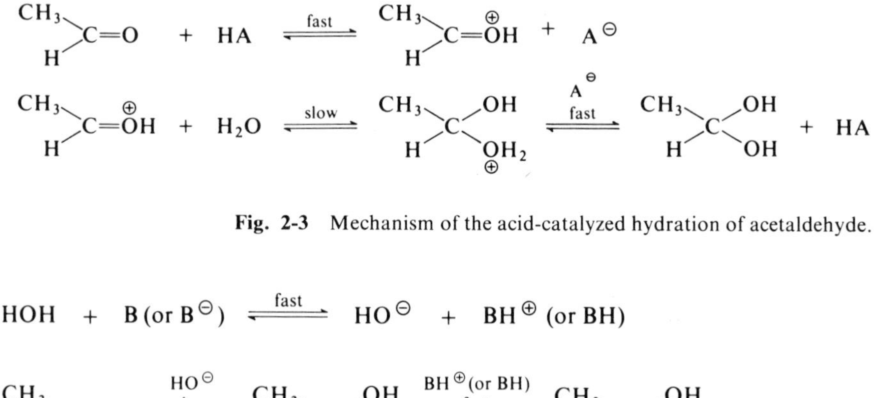

Fig. 2-3 Mechanism of the acid-catalyzed hydration of acetaldehyde.

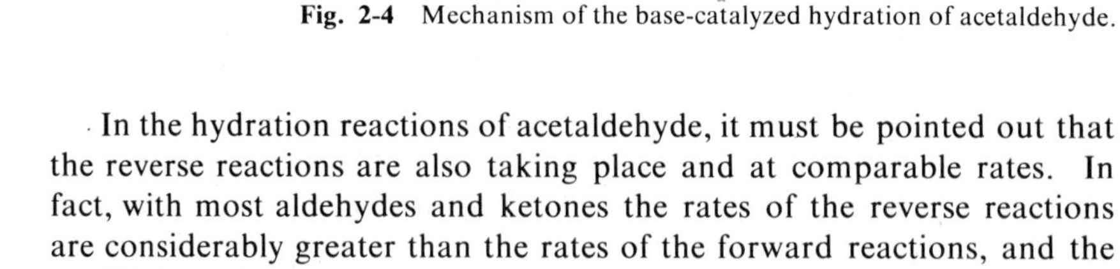

Fig. 2-4 Mechanism of the base-catalyzed hydration of acetaldehyde.

In the hydration reactions of acetaldehyde, it must be pointed out that the reverse reactions are also taking place and at comparable rates. In fact, with most aldehydes and ketones the rates of the reverse reactions are considerably greater than the rates of the forward reactions, and the equilibrium does not favor the hydrate. It is important to keep in mind that there is no necessary correlation between the rate of the forward reaction and the extent of product formation. Olefins, for instance, are completely inert to water at pH 7, presumably a consequence of the nonpolar character of the C=C bond. Bond energy calculations,† however, show that the hydration product (i.e., the alcohol) is more stable than the olefin by about 14 kcal/mole. Indeed, olefins are easily and completely converted to alcohols by acid-catalyzed hydration. Aldehydes, on the other hand, *will* interact with water at pH 7, albeit slowly, to form a hydration product, presumably as a consequence of the strongly polar character of the C=O bond. Bond energy calculations in this case indicate that the hydration product is *less* stable than the aldehyde by about 5 kcal/mole (see Fig. 2-5). It is clear, then, that organic chemists interested in the

Table 2-1

SOME USEFUL BOND ENERGY VALUES

Bond type	Energy in kcal/mole
C—H	99
N—H	93
O—H	111
C—C	83
C—N	73
C—O	85.5
C=C	146
C=N	147
C=O (aldehydes)	176
C=O (ketones)	179
C≡C	200
C≡N	213

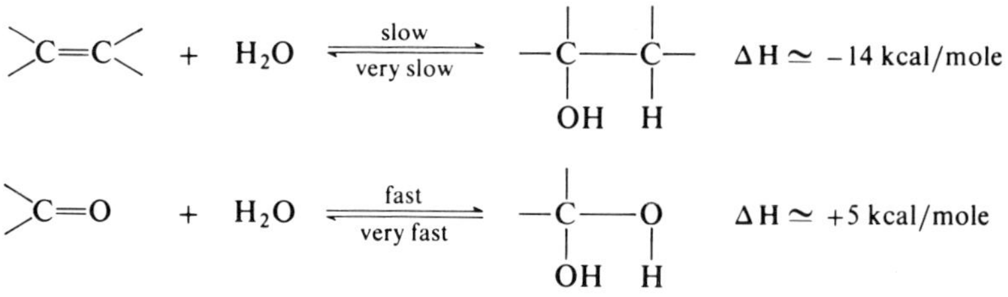

synthetic usefulness of a reaction must be concerned with the rates of forward *and* reverse reactions and must seek means for increasing the former and minimizing the effect of the latter. The increase in rate may

$$\text{>C=C<} + H_2O \underset{\text{very slow}}{\overset{\text{slow}}{\rightleftharpoons}} \text{—C—C—} \quad \Delta H \simeq -14 \text{ kcal/mole}$$
$$\text{OH} \quad \text{H}$$

$$\text{>C=O} + H_2O \underset{\text{very fast}}{\overset{\text{fast}}{\rightleftharpoons}} \text{—C—O} \quad \Delta H \simeq +5 \text{ kcal/mole}$$
$$\text{OH} \quad \text{H}$$

Fig. 2-5 Kinetic and thermodynamic comparisons of hydration reactions.

be brought about with appropriate catalysts; it should be emphasized, however, that the effect of this is simply to establish equilibrium more rapidly but not to change the position of the equilibrium. To minimize the effect of the reverse reaction and an adverse equilibrium constant, various means of product removal may be used. Numerous examples of appropriate methods will appear throughout the book.

A process which is more favorable than hydration to the formation of addition product is the interaction of hydrogen cyanide with aldehydes and ketones to yield cyanohydrins. This reaction is catalyzed by bases such as amines and cyanide ion, and it is proposed that (a) the basic catalyst interacts with hydrogen cyanide in a rapid proton transfer reaction to generate the cyanide ion (nucleophilic species), (b) the nucleophilic addition of cyanide ion to the carbonyl group takes place in a slow step, and

† See Table 2-1 and N. L. Allinger and J. Allinger, *op. cit.*

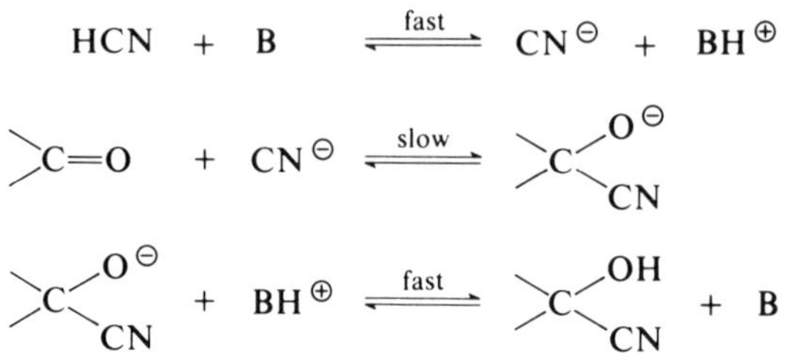

$$HCN + B \underset{}{\overset{fast}{\rightleftarrows}} CN^{\ominus} + BH^{\oplus}$$

$$\ce{>C=O} + CN^{\ominus} \underset{}{\overset{slow}{\rightleftarrows}} \ce{>C<_{CN}^{O^{\ominus}}}$$

$$\ce{>C<_{CN}^{O^{\ominus}}} + BH^{\oplus} \underset{}{\overset{fast}{\rightleftarrows}} \ce{>C<_{CN}^{OH}} + B$$

Fig. 2-6 Mechanism of cyanohydrin formation.

(c) a second rapid proton transfer occurs to complete the conversion to the cyanohydrin, as shown in Fig. 2-6. The equilibrium constants for a number of carbonyl-cyanohydrin systems have been measured (see Table 2-2 for representative cases), and these provide one gauge of the "carbonyl character" of a particular carbonyl compound. The greater the cyanohydrin formation constant, the more reactive is the carbonyl compound (in the sense of product formation) and, by this definition, the more carbonyl character it possesses. Thus, acetaldehyde (high formation constant) is strongly carbonyl-like in character; benzaldehyde, methyl ethyl ketone, and acetophenone (smaller formation constants) are somewhat less carbonyl-like; and certain members of class AC carbonyl compounds (close to zero formation constants) are a great deal less carbonyl-like.

The extent of cyanohydrin formation is interpretable in terms of electronic and steric factors. The difference in the equilibrium constant for acetaldehyde and methyl ethyl ketone, for example, is primarily due to steric influences. The ethyl group is very much more space-filling than is a hydrogen atom, and, as a result, a bond-forming collision between the carbonyl group and the cyanide ion requires more energy (enthalpy factor) and a more restricted path of approach (entropy factor). This reduces the rate of the forward reaction. Conversely, the rate of the reverse reaction is greater for the cyanohydrin of methyl ethyl ketone than for the cyanohydrin of acetaldehyde because of the greater steric interference around the carbon in the former and the greater extent to

Table 2-2

FORMATION CONSTANTS FOR CYANOHYDRINS

Compound	Formation constant
CH_3CHO	too large to measure
p-Nitrobenzaldehyde	1430
Benzaldehyde	210
p-Methoxybenzaldehyde	32
p-Dimethylaminobenzaldehyde	2.6
Cyclopentanone	500
Cyclohexanone	10,000
Cycloheptanone	75
$CH_3COCH_2CH_3$	38
$C_6H_5COCH_3$	0.77
$C_6H_5COC_6H_5$	too small to measure
$CH_3CO_2C_2H_5$	too small to measure

which this strain is relieved upon reverting to the carbonyl compound. The obvious result of a decreased forward rate and an increased reverse rate is a diminished equilibrium constant for product formation. The difference between methyl ethyl ketone and acetophenone, on the other hand, is only partly to be ascribed to steric factors (i.e., phenyl is somewhat more space-filling than ethyl) and must also involve an electronic factor. Acetophenone, a member of class **AB** compounds, carries a phenyl group attached to the carbonyl group, and this allows the electron deficiency at the carbonyl carbon to be delocalized into the aromatic ring (see Sec. 1.7). The diminished electron deficiency at the carbonyl carbon reduces its attraction for a nucleophilic species and requires a higher energy collision for bond formation (enthalpy factor). Stated in terms of free energy changes ($\ln K = -\Delta G/RT$), the magnitude of $-\Delta G$ is greater for the addition to methyl ethyl ketone than to acetophenone, because in the latter case there is a greater loss of resonance energy in progressing from carbonyl compound to product. This is the result of the far greater ability of an sp^2 hybridized carbon atom (i.e., the carbonyl carbon), as compared with an sp^3 hybridized carbon atom (i.e., the cyanohydrin carbon), to engage in orbital overlap with an aromatic ring. Thus, acetophenone has more to lose than does methyl ethyl ketone in undergoing the $sp^2 \rightarrow sp^3$ conversion.

To study the electronic factor untainted by the steric factor is frequently difficult, but may be achieved in the case of *para*-substituted benzaldehydes. Changes in the *para* substituent can have little effect on the aldehyde group through steric interaction, but may have a strong influence via electronic transmission through the benzene ring. Since the facility of nucleophilic addition depends upon the magnitude of the electron deficiency at the carbonyl carbon, it would be anticipated that electron-releasing substituents would interfere with the reaction and that electron-withdrawing substituents would facilitate the reaction. This is exactly what is observed. For instance, *p*-methoxybenzaldehyde (methoxyl group is electron-releasing via the resonance-electromeric route) has a lower cyanohydrin formation constant than benzaldehyde, while *p*-nitrobenzaldehyde (nitro group is electron-withdrawing via the resonance-electromeric route as well as via the inductive route) has a higher cyanohydrin formation constant.

The synthesis of semicarbazones by treatment of aldehydes or ketones with semicarbazide (see Fig. 2-7) is a good example of a reaction which can be driven in the direction of product in spite of an unfavorable carbonyl addition step. The process takes place in two stages, the first involving direct carbonyl addition and the second involving a dehydration. Bond energy calculations indicate the first step to be slightly endothermic (ΔH is about 0 to $+3$ kcal/mole) and the second step to be fairly exothermic (ΔH is about -4 to -7 kcal/mole), making the overall

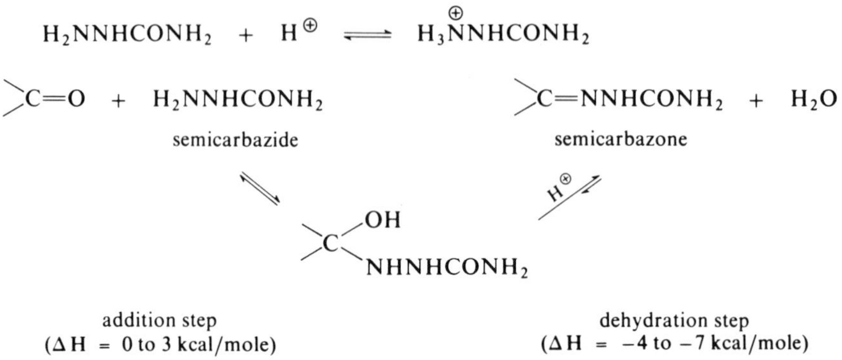

$$H_2NNHCONH_2 \; + \; H^{\oplus} \; \rightleftharpoons \; H_3\overset{\oplus}{N}NHCONH_2$$

$$\ce{>C=O} \; + \; H_2NNHCONH_2 \qquad\qquad \ce{>C=NNHCONH_2} \; + \; H_2O$$

semicarbazide   semicarbazone

$$\ce{>C<^{OH}_{NHNHCONH_2}}$$

addition step	dehydration step
($\Delta H = 0$ to 3 kcal/mole)	($\Delta H = -4$ to -7 kcal/mole)

Fig. 2-7 Mechanism of semicarbazone formation.

reaction thermodynamically favorable with ΔH equal to approximately -4 kcal/mole. For the reaction to proceed readily, however, it is necessary that the acidity be properly adjusted, for the individual steps depend on the availability of protons in different ways. The second step is strongly acid-catalyzed and in acid medium is so fast that the addition step becomes the rate-limiting one. The first step, also, is acid catalyzed, insofar as protonation of the carbonyl group enhances the electrophilic character of the carbonyl carbon. The nucleophilic species (semicarbazide), however, is a stronger base than the carbonyl group and is much more readily protonated, thereby losing its nucleophilic capacity. It is necessary, then, to find a pH at which the acid-catalyzed dehydration will proceed rapidly, and at which there is an adequate concentration of free semicarbazide present. In practice this is achieved by maintaining the reaction mixture at about pH 4.

For a given carbonyl compound, the position of the equilibrium in a nucleophilic addition reaction is dependent on the nucleophilic reagent. As the nucleophilic center changes from oxygen to nitrogen to carbon, the equilibrium shifts to the right as indicated by the bond energy calculations shown in Fig. 2-8. Nucleophilic reagents stronger than cyanide ion should

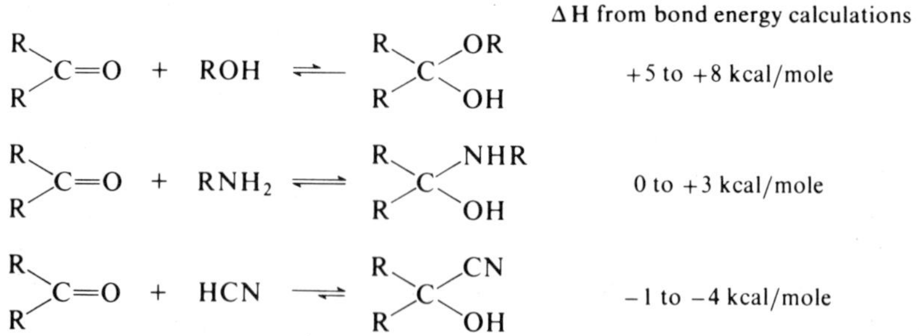

ΔH from bond energy calculations

$$\ce{R2C=O} \; + \; ROH \; \rightleftharpoons \; \ce{R2C<^{OR}_{OH}} \qquad +5 \text{ to } +8 \text{ kcal/mole}$$

$$\ce{R2C=O} \; + \; RNH_2 \; \rightleftharpoons \; \ce{R2C<^{NHR}_{OH}} \qquad 0 \text{ to } +3 \text{ kcal/mole}$$

$$\ce{R2C=O} \; + \; HCN \; \rightleftharpoons \; \ce{R2C<^{CN}_{OH}} \qquad -1 \text{ to } -4 \text{ kcal/mole}$$

Fig. 2-8 Equilibria in nucleophilic addition reactions.

push the addition reaction even further to completion. Organometallic compounds such as Grignard reagents represent a source of powerful nucleophilic reagents, and these do in fact add very effectively to most carbonyl compounds (see Chap. 4).

On the basis of various studies of the direct addition reaction of carbonyl compounds, it appears that addition product is favored by: (a) small R groups attached to the carbonyl group; (b) strong nucleophilic reagents such as $RMgX$; (c) electron-attracting (via the inductive or the resonance-electromeric route) groups attached to the carbonyl group. The last effect has been ascribed to the reduction in dipole opposition that follows from the transformation of a carbonyl group to a tetrahedrally-substituted carbon, as illustrated in Fig. 2-9 for the formation of the hydrate of chloral.

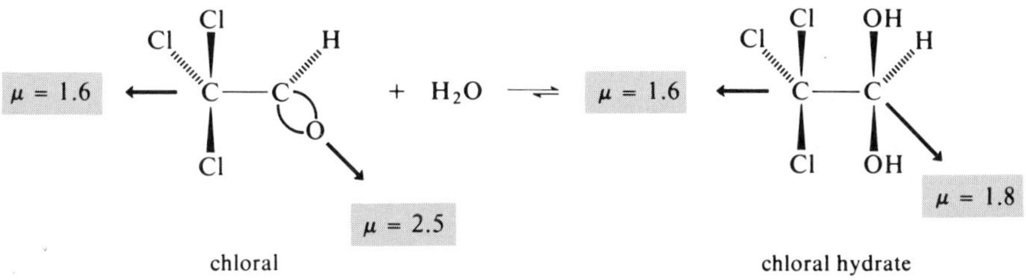

Fig. 2-9   Comparison of dipole opposition in chloral and chloral hydrate.

2.3 INDIRECT OR CONJUGATE ADDITION

A carbon-carbon multiple bond attached to a carbonyl group allows the electron deficiency of the carbonyl carbon to be partially transferred to a more remote position (see Secs. 1.7 and 1.9). If the unsaturation is part of an aromatic ring, the result in most cases is simply to reduce the reactivity of the carbonyl group without changing the point of nucleophilic attack, namely, at the carbonyl carbon. If the unsaturation is a simple $C{=}C$ bond, however, not only may the carbonyl reactivity at the carbonyl carbon be reduced, but the point of nucleophilic attack may also be changed. For instance, methyl vinyl ketone can react with hydrogen cyanide in two fashions: at low temperatures direct addition takes place to yield the cyanohydrin, while at room temperature conjugate addition takes place to give γ-ketovaleronitrile. Benzalacetophenone undergoes only conjugate addition to yield α-phenyl-β-benzoylpropionitrile. Ethyl crotonate, a class BC compound which contains a carbonyl group which is unreactive to hydrogen cyanide by direct addition, nevertheless undergoes conjugate addition to give ethyl β-cyanobutyrate. Fig. 2-10 illustrates these several reactions.

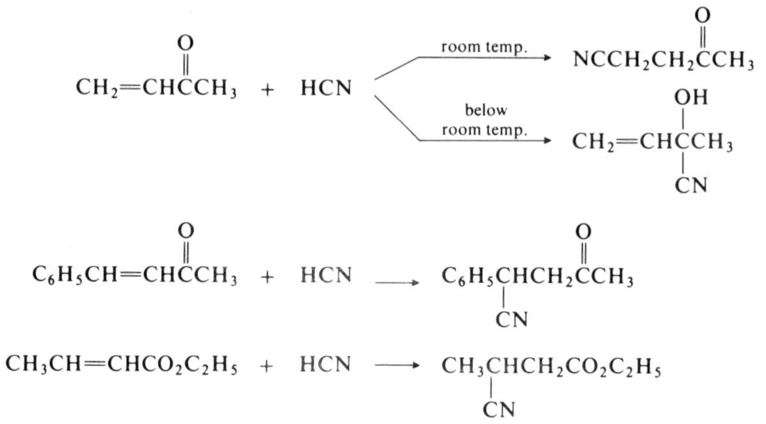

$$CH_2{=}CHCCH_3 \ + \ HCN \quad \xrightarrow[\text{below room temp.}]{\text{room temp.}} \quad \begin{array}{l} NCCH_2CH_2CCH_3 \\[4pt] OH \\ CH_2{=}CHCCH_3 \\ CN \end{array}$$

$$C_6H_5CH{=}CHCCH_3 \ + \ HCN \ \longrightarrow \ C_6H_5CHCH_2CCH_3$$
$$CN$$

$$CH_3CH{=}CHCO_2C_2H_5 \ + \ HCN \ \longrightarrow \ CH_3CHCH_2CO_2C_2H_5$$
$$CN$$

Fig. 2-10 Reaction of α,β-unsaturated carbonyl compounds with hydrogen cyanide.

The general mechanism by which conjugate addition is postulated to take place is illustrated in Fig. 2-11. The nucleophilic species, instead of attacking the carbonyl carbon as in direct addition, attacks a more remote position to which a part of the electron deficiency has been transferred.

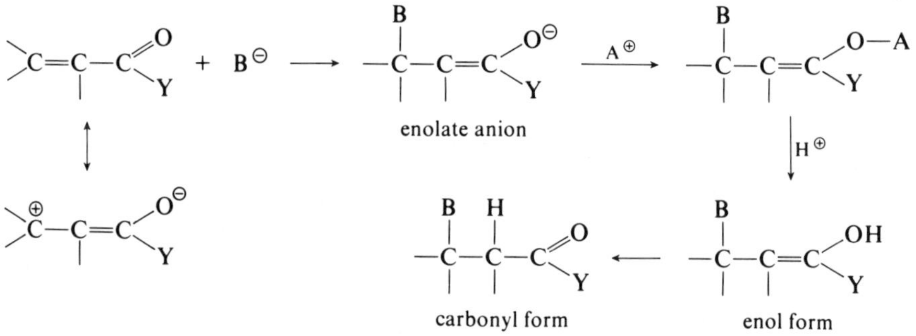

Fig. 2-11 Mechanism of conjugate addition to α,β-unsaturated carbonyl compounds.

Annexation of the electrophilic species (occurring after the nucleophilic addition in the case of a base-catalyzed reaction) then produces an enolate compound. In a nonproton containing solvent the enolate may be stable, but upon acquiring a proton it reverts to the carbonyl form (see keto-enol equilibria in Sec. 1.11). The *apparent* course of a reaction of this type, then, is a 1,2-addition across a carbon-carbon multiple bond, but the *actual* course is a 1,4- (or 1, 6,- etc.) addition in which the nucleophilic species attaches itself to the 4-position (or the 6-position, etc.), and the electrophilic species to the carbonyl oxygen (the 1-position).[†]

Bond energy calculations for 1,2- and 1,4-addition processes indicate that the latter should be favored by a considerable amount. In spite of this, however, direct addition (i.e., 1,2-addition) reactions with α,β-unsaturated carbonyl compounds are frequently observed. For instance, mesityl oxide reacts with methyl amine via conjugate addition but with ethylmagnesium bromide via direct addition, as illustrated in Fig. 2-12.

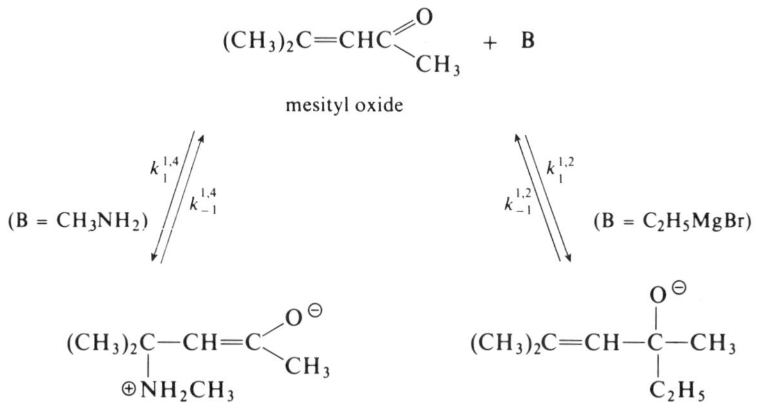

$$(CH_3)_2C{=}CHC\overset{O}{\underset{CH_3}{\diagdown}} \quad + \quad B$$

mesityl oxide

$k_1^{1,4}$ $k_{-1}^{1,4}$ $(B = CH_3NH_2)$ $k_{-1}^{1,2}$ $k_1^{1,2}$ $(B = C_2H_5MgBr)$

$$(CH_3)_2C{-}CH{=}C\overset{O^{\ominus}}{\underset{CH_3}{\diagdown}}$$
$$\underset{\oplus NH_2CH_3}{|}$$

$$(CH_3)_2C{=}CH{-}\underset{\underset{C_2H_5}{|}}{\overset{\overset{O^{\ominus}}{|}}{C}}{-}CH_3$$

Fig. 2-12   Nucleophilic addition reactions of mesityl oxide.

The tendency for stronger nucleophiles such as ethylmagnesium bromide to undergo 1,2-addition, and weaker nucleophiles such as methyl amine to undergo 1,4-addition, may be interpreted in terms of a general principle which will be applicable in several succeeding instances as well. As has been discussed in other volumes of this series,[‡] the course of a reaction can be described in terms of a "reaction coordinate" which depicts the change in energy of a system as it passes from reactant through transition state to product. The position of the transition state may vary along the horizontal coordinate; if it lies close to reactant its structure resembles that of the reactant, while if it lies close to product its structure resembles that of product (see Fig. 2-13). The sensitivity of any particular reaction to structural features in reactant or product will determine the position of the transition state on this coordinate. For transition states lying close to reactant, electrostatic factors (i.e., charge localization) are often dominant

† The general term "conjugate addition" is used for this type of reaction. Synonymously, the terms "1,4-addition," "1,6-addition," etc. can be employed and are sometimes preferable in being explicit as to the separation in numbers of atoms between the reaction termini of the conjugated system.

‡ W. H. Saunders, Jr., op. cit; R. Stewart, op. cit.

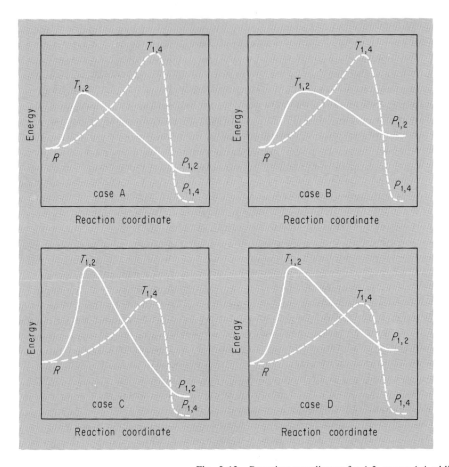

Fig. 2-13 Reaction coordinates for 1,2- versus 1,4-addition.

in determining the ease with which the transition state is reached and, hence, the rate at which the reaction proceeds. Conversely, for transition states lying close to product, electrostatic factors become *less* crucial, and the strength of the newly forming bond assumes major importance. In a compound such as mesityl oxide, it is reasonable to assume that the point of maximum electron deficiency is the carbonyl carbon (in spite of the partial transference of this deficiency to the β-carbon). A powerful nucleophile such as $C_2H_5^{\ominus}$ (from $C_2H_5 MgBr$) will be strongly attracted to this position; it can lift the system to a transition state in which the formation of the new bond has scarcely started and in which the influence of bonding in the product is but scarcely felt. A weak nucleophile such as methyl amine, on the other hand, is not as strongly attracted by charge deficiency per se and cannot elevate the system to the transition state except by coming almost within bonding distance of the atom with which it seeks to form a bond, i.e., to give a transition state which resembles product.

If it is assumed that the product of 1,4-addition ($P_{1,4}$) is always more stable than reactant (R), but that the product of 1,2-addition ($P_{1,2}$) may or may not be more stable than reactant, the four reaction coordinate diagrams illustrated in Fig. 2-13 are possible. The transition state for 1,2-addition ($T_{1,2}$) will be lower in energy than the transition state for 1,4-addition ($T_{1,4}$) in the case of strong nucleophiles and will lead to 1,2-addition product if $P_{1,2}$ is more stable than R (case A in Fig. 2-13). A product arising from this circumstance is said to be one of "kinetic control." However, if $P_{1,2}$ is less stable than R (case B in Fig. 2-13), the 1,4-addition product will accumulate in spite of the fact that it is formed less rapidly than $P_{1,2}$. A product arising from this circumstance is said to be one of "thermodynamic control," and some 1,4-addition reactions may be explained in these terms. Alternatively, the transition state for 1,4-addition may be lower in energy than the transition state for 1,2-addition in the case of weak nucleophiles (cases C and D in Fig. 2-13). In these instances, the product of 1,4-addition is that of *both* kinetic *and* thermodynamic control.

For a given nucleophile the extent of reaction along the direct addition and conjugate addition pathways will be governed by steric and electronic factors. The latter is illustrated by the comparison of ethyl cinnamate (Fig. 2-14, R = H), which undergoes direct addition with methylmagnesium bromide, and ethyl benzalmalonate (Fig. 2-14, R = $CO_2C_2H_5$), which undergoes conjugate addition with this same reagent. In the latter case, each ester carbonyl is individually no more reactive to direct addition than the ester carbonyl of ethyl cinnamate; the transmission of electron deficiency to the β-position by the *combined* efforts of the two carbethoxy groups, however, is greater than in ethyl cinnamate. The interplay of steric factors is illustrated by the data presented in Table 2-3, which indicate that hindrance in the vicinity of the carbonyl group facilitates direct addition. The reactivities at the carbonyl carbon and the β-carbon may also be sensitive to subtle changes in the nucleophile. For example, benzalacetophenone reacts with phenylmagnesium bromide to

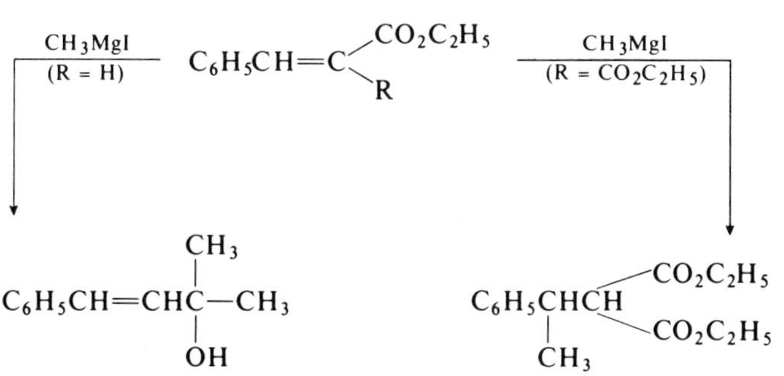

Fig. 2-14 Direct and conjugate addition of methylmagnesium bromide.

give 88% of direct addition product (see Table 2-3) but with ethylmagnesium bromide to give only 40% of direct addition product and 60% of conjugate addition product. The following generalizations for direct addition versus conjugate addition can be stated: (a) direct addition product increases with increasing strength of the nucleophile; (b) conjugate addition increases with decreasing "carbonyl character" of the carbonyl group; (c) conjugate addition increases with increasing steric hindrance at the carbonyl group; (d) direct addition increases with increasing steric hindrance at the β-position. Some additional factors controlling direct and conjugate addition are discussed on page 80.

Table 2-3

REACTION OF PHENYLMAGNESIUM BROMIDE WITH α,β-UNSATURATED COMPOUNDS

Compound	% Direct addition	% Conjugate addition
$C_6H_5CH=CHCHO$	100	0
$C_6H_5CH=CHCOCH_3$	88	12
$C_6H_5CH=CHCOCH_2CH_3$	60	40
$C_6H_5CH=CHCOCH(CH_3)_2$	12	88
$C_6H_5CH=CHCOC_6H_5$	6	94
$C_6H_5CH=CHCOC(CH_3)_3$	0	100
$C_6H_5C=CHCOC_6H_5$ $\mid$ CH_3	56	44

2.4 NUCLEOPHILIC ADDITION-ELIMINATION

The terminating step in the direct addition reaction is the acquisition of a proton in the base-catalyzed reaction or the loss of a proton in the acid-catalyzed reaction (see Fig. 2-3 and Fig. 2-4). An alternative mode of stabilization for the intermediates is illustrated in Fig. 2-15 and involves the elimination of a Y group ($Y^\ominus$ in base, YH + $H^\oplus$ in acid) with regeneration of a carbonyl function. Whether or not this latter path is followed depends on the nature of the Y group. In class AA, AB, and BB compounds the C—Y bond is a carbon-carbon bond; since carbon does not easily sustain a negative charge, the cleavage of this bond (with the expulsion of a carbanion) does not occur readily, and only direct addition is observed. If the Y group is a hetero atom, however, it *can* more readily accommodate a negative charge and is, therefore, more readily expelled. Thus, compounds of class AC, BC, and CC (where the Y group is halogen, OR, NR$_2$, etc.) may follow the addition-elimination pathway; in fact, this is the characteristic reaction of compounds in this group.

The most thoroughly studied addition-elimination reaction of carbonyl compounds is that of ester hydrolysis. There are several reasonable

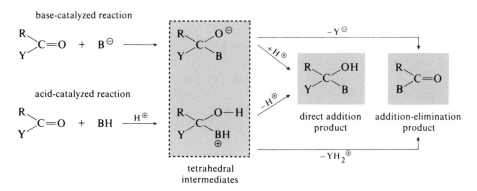

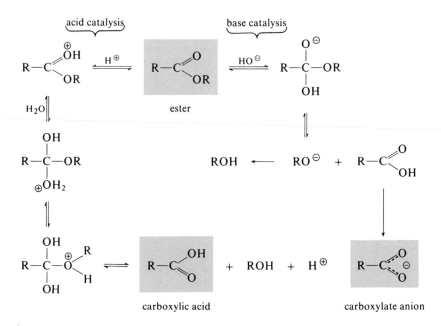

Fig. 2-15 Nucleophilic addition-elimination reaction.

mechanistic pathways by means of which ester hydrolysis can take place, and most of these have been observed. For the present discussion, however, only two mechanisms will be considered, both involving a nucleophilic addition to the carbonyl group. These are the acid-catalyzed and and base-catalyzed bimolecular hydrolyses of the type shown in Fig. 2-16. It has been adequately demonstrated by kinetic analysis and by O^{18} tracer studies that reactions which are assumed to take place by the mechanisms depicted in Fig. 2-16 do indeed involve a nucleophilic addition to the carbonyl group to give a *tetrahedral intermediate* (i.e., the carbonyl

Fig. 2-16 Acid-catalyzed and base-catalyzed hydrolyses of esters.

carbon has become sp^3 hybridized). It is not surprising, then, to find a correspondence in the steric and electronic factors for direct addition (e.g., cyanohydrin formation) and addition-elimination (e.g., ester hydrolysis). Thus, the ratios of hydrolysis rates, $RCO_2C_2H_5/CH_3CO_2C_2H_5$, decline in the order $CH_3CO_2C_2H_5$ (1.00), $CH_3CH_2CO_2C_2H_5$ (0.47), $(CH_3)_2CHCO_2C_2H_5$ (0.10), $(CH_3)_3CCO_2C_2H_5$ (0.01) as the result of increasing steric hindrance to the incoming nucleophile; the ratios of hydrolysis rates, $X—C_6H_4CO_2C_2H_5/H—C_6H_4CO_2C_2H_5$, decline in the

order O_2N—⟨○⟩—$CO_2C_2H_5$ (110), H—⟨○⟩—$CO_2C_2H_5$ (1.00),

CH_3O—⟨○⟩—$CO_2C_2H_5$ (0.21) as the result of electronic transmission

from the *p*-substituent to the carbonyl group.

In addition to ester hydrolysis, a variety of mechanistically similar reactions are known and are often grouped under the heading of "-olysis reactions"; these include alcoholysis, acidolysis, aminolysis, etc. They all follow the addition-elimination pathway shown in Fig. 2-15 and are classified according to the identity of the incoming nucleophile (B) and the displaced group (Y). Except in the special case of base-promoted hydrolysis, which forms the carboxylate ion, reactions in this group are more or less reversible, and the equilibrium constant is dependent on the nature of B and Y. The ease of displacement of the Y moiety in RCOY is reciprocal to its nucleophilic character and increases as one progresses from the middle to the right of the periodic table, i.e., $Y = R_3C^\ominus < R_2N^\ominus <$
$$RC{\overset{O}{\diagup}}{\underset{NR^\ominus}{\diagdown}} < RO^\ominus < RC{\overset{O}{\diagup}}{\underset{O}{\diagdown}}\,{}^\ominus < X^\ominus.$$ Numerous examples, many of significant value for organic syntheses, support these reactivity data. Thus, acid chlorides can be converted in essentially irreversible reactions to anhydrides (displacement by $RCO_2^\ominus$), to esters (displacement by $RO^\ominus$), and amides (displacement by $R_2N^\ominus$); anhydrides can be converted to esters and to amides (but not readily to acid halides); esters can be converted to amides (but not readily to acid halides or anhydrides).

Although most of the examples of the nucleophilic addition-elimination reaction occur with members of class AC, BC, and CC carbonyl compounds, certain types of class AA compounds may also undergo this reaction. The essential requirement is that the carbon attached to the carbonyl function carry groups which facilitate the accumulation of a negative charge. The most common ones possessing this ability are halogen atoms and carbonyl functions. Thus, α,α,α-trihaloketones and β-dicarbonyl compounds undergo base-induced cleavage in the manner shown in Fig. 2-17. The ability to undergo the addition-elimination reaction is characteristic of but not unique to class AC, BC, and CC compounds. It is clear from the above examples that the difference between

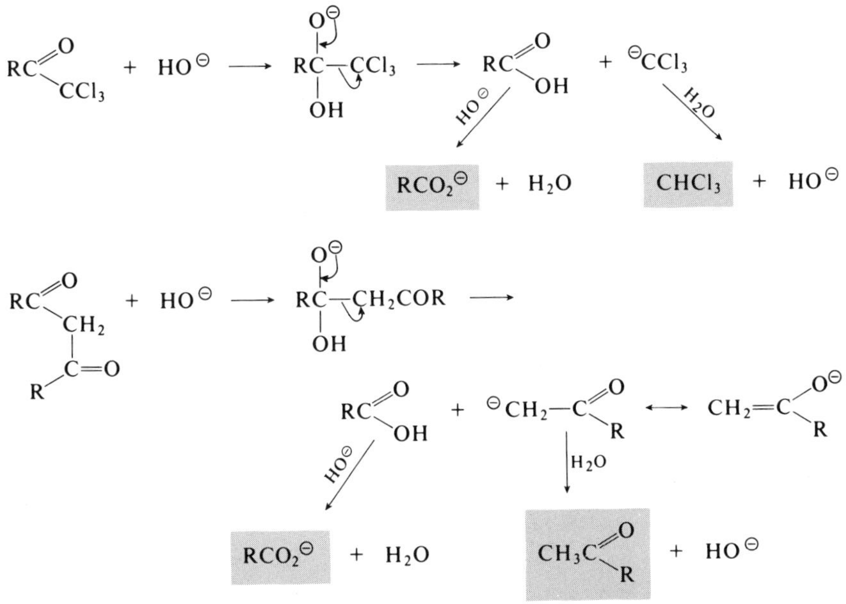

Fig. 2-17 Nucleophilic addition-elimination in class AA compounds.

classes AA, AB, and BB on the one hand, and classes AC, BC, and CC on the other hand, is a quantitative rather than a qualitative one.

The great majority of nucleophilic addition-elimination reactions follow the course illustrated in Fig. 2-15. Alternative modes of elimination are sometimes possible, however, in cases where displaceable functions are present elsewhere in the carbonyl compound or are carried in by the nucleophilic reagent. Three pathways, henceforth specified as type Z addition-elimination reactions, are illustrated in Fig. 2-18; specific examples will be discussed in Chaps. 3 and 4.

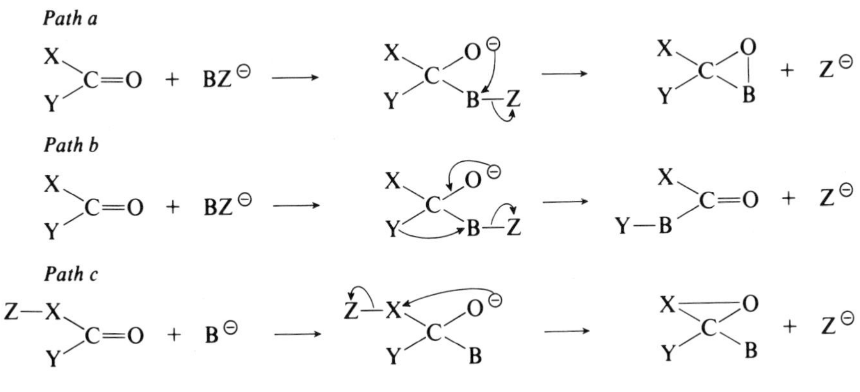

Fig. 2-18 Type Z addition-elimination reactions.

2.5 STEREOCHEMISTRY OF CARBONYL ADDITION REACTIONS

Except with formaldehyde and symmetrical ketones such as acetone, the two faces of a carbonyl group are not identical, and attack of a nucleophilic reagent can give two stereochemically different products. For compounds of the general structure $RR'C=O$, in which neither the R or R' group is dissymmetric, the difference between the faces of the carbonyl group is an enantiomeric one, and the products of addition of a nucleophile are nonsuperimposable mirror images, as represented in Fig. 2-19.

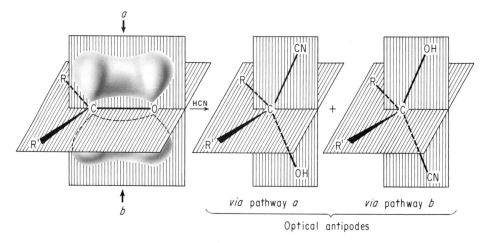

Fig. 2-19 The stereochemistry of the nucleophilic addition to an $RR'C=O$ carbonyl compound (R and R' nondissymmetric).

In a symmetrical environment[†] the optical antipodes are formed in exactly equal amounts, and the product is optically inactive. If R and/or R' is dissymmetric, however, the difference between the faces of the carbonyl group is a diastereoisomeric one, and the products of nucleophilic addition are diastereoisomers of each other, as represented in Fig. 2-20.[‡]

The addition of hydrogen cyanide to bicyclo [2.2.1] heptan-2-one (Fig. 2-20, $B^\ominus = CN^\ominus$) yields unequal amounts of two cyanohydrins which differ in physical properties and which are separable by ordinary chemical means. The product ratio of such a reaction mixture will be determined either by the relative rates of reaction along pathways a and b (kinetic

---

[†] An optically active solvent or, in the case of cyanohydrin formation, an optically active base catalyst would constitute an asymmetric environment and might lead to optically active product.

[‡] Here, also, the products are optically inactive if the starting material is optically inactive. If optically active ketone is used, both diastereoisomeric products are optically active. They are not mirror images, however, and will differ in physical properties including the magnitudes of rotation.

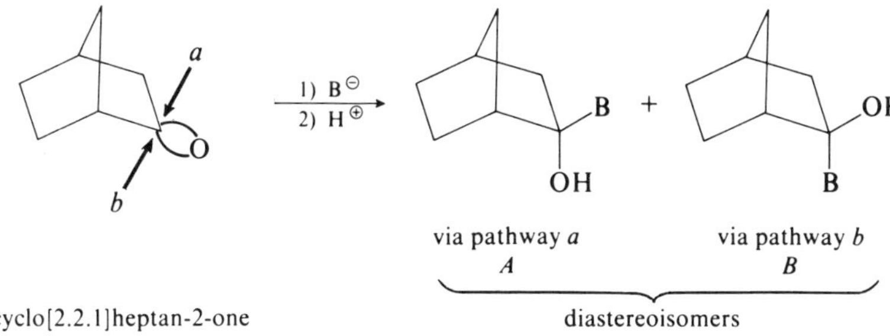

via pathway *a*   via pathway *b*
         A   B

bicyclo[2.2.1]heptan-2-one   diastereoisomers

Fig. 2-20 The stereochemistry of the nucleophilic addition to an
$RR'C{=}O$ carbonyl compound (R and R′ dissymmetric).

control) or by the relative stabilities of the products formed (thermodynamic control). In the case of cyanohydrin formation, the latter is the
controlling factor, for the reaction is a readily reversible one (see Figs.
2-6 and 2-13). With a Grignard reagent (Fig. 2-20, $B^{\ominus} = R^{\ominus}$ of RMgX),
however, kinetic product control is more likely; path *a* is more sterically
accessible than path *b*, and the product of structure *A* will be predomi-
nant. This is an easy prediction in the example cited, because the carbonyl
group is contained in a rigid system. Such predictions become more difficult when the carbonyl group is contained in a flexible system, however.
A study of the stereochemical course of a large number of nucleophilic
additions (primarily involving Grignard reagents) has led to a predictive
scheme which is usually referred to as the rule of asymmetric induction.
The assumptions involved in the application of this rule are (a) of the con-
formations conducive to reaction, one will be of lowest energy, and (b) in
this lowest energy reactive conformation, one face of the carbonyl group
will be less hindered than the other. The preferred reactive conformation
is generally that one in which the carbonyl group is flanked by the two
least bulky groups which are attached to the neighboring carbon atom.
In the case of 3-phenyl-2-propanone, for instance, the preferred reactive
conformation would be the one shown in Fig. 2-21, and the major product
of reaction with phenylmagnesium bromide would be predicted to be the
one resulting from the approach of the nucleophile at the less hindered
face, *a*.

On the basis of existing data, certain approximate rules concerning
the stereochemical course of nucleophilic addition reactions can be stated:
(a) the product of kinetic control becomes favored as the difference in
hindrance at the two faces of the carbonyl group increases; (b) the product
of kinetic control becomes favored as the bulk of the nucleophilic reagent
increases and magnifies the steric differences between the two faces of the
carbonyl group; (c) the product of kinetic control appears to become
favored as the nucleophilic character of the nucleophile increases (e.g.
Grignard reagents are most likely to give the product of kinetic control).

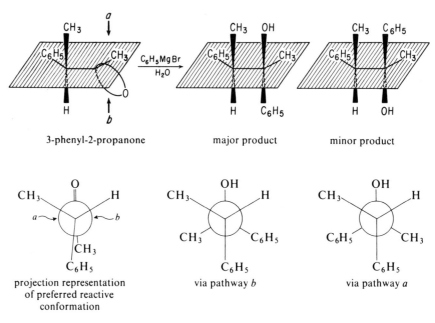

Fig. 2-21 Illustration of the rule of asymmetric induction.

The interaction of nucleophiles with carbonyl compounds via direct addition, conjugate addition, and addition-elimination are extremely important reactions from the standpoint of preparative organic chemistry, and thousands of examples have been reported in the chemical literature. The following chapters will attempt to survey this large body of information in such a way as to emphasize the synthetic usefulness of these reactions.

PROBLEMS

1. Arrange the following compounds in the order of increasing association constant for the formation of cyanohydrin:

a. CH_3COCH_3, $ClCH_2COCH_3$, $C_6H_5COC_6H_5$, $C_6H_5COCH_3$

b.

2. Arrange the following compounds in the order of increasing rate of base-induced ester hydrolysis:

a. $Cl_2CHCO_2CH_2CH_3$, $CH_3CO_2CH_3$, $(CH_3)_3CCO_2CH_3$, $CH_3CO_2C(CH_3)_3$

b. CH_3COCl, $(CH_3CO)_2O$, $CH_3CO_2CH_2CH_3$, CH_3CONH_2

c. 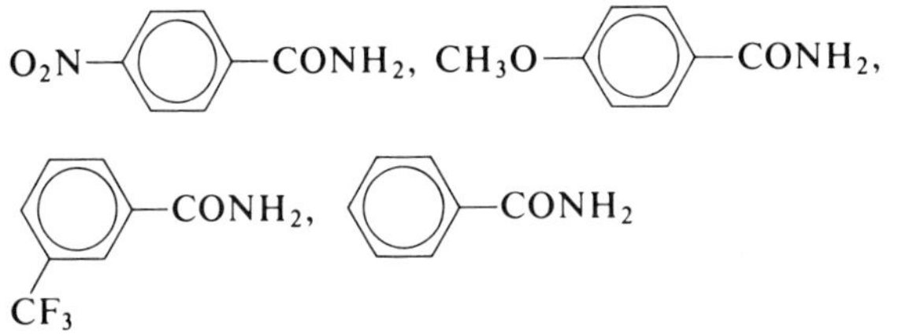 O_2N—⬡—$CONH_2$, CH_3O—⬡—$CONH_2$,

⬡—$CONH_2$, ⬡—$CONH_2$
|
CF_3

3. Water labeled with deuterium in place of hydrogen (i.e., D_2O) or with O^{18} in place of O^{16} (i.e., H_2O^{18}) has been useful in many studies of reaction mechanisms. Outline experiments which could make use of these materials in the (a) deduction of a tetrahedral intermediate in the acid-catalyzed hydrolysis of esters, (b) the rate of enolization of 2,6-dimethylcyclohexanone, (c) the relative rates of enolization and hydrate formation of acetone.

4. Explain the following observations:

a. Semicarbazones are better carbonyl derivatives for purposes of product characterization than are cyanohydrins.

b. The pH optimum for oxime formation (from NH_2OH) is somewhat different from that for semicarbazone formation (from NH_2-$NHCONH_2$).

c. Acid chlorides can be prepared by the action of thionyl chloride on carboxylic acids in spite of the fact that the equilibrium between RCO_2H and $RCOCl$ favors the former.

d. Acid amides can be converted to esters by the action of an alcohol on the amide in the presence of relatively large amounts of mineral acid.

e. The reaction shown below is a useful method for preparing ketals (see p. 48), because the equilibrium constant is greater than unity.

$$HC(OC_2H_5)_3 + R_2C=O \underset{\rightleftharpoons}{\overset{H^\oplus}{}} HCO_2C_2H_5 + R_2C(OC_2H_5)_2$$

5. Draw and label (e.g., optically active, racemic, or meso) the cyanohydrin products from the following reactions:

a.

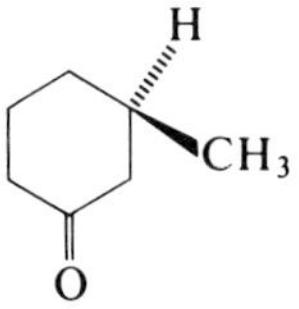

+ HCN → mono-cyanohydrin products

b.

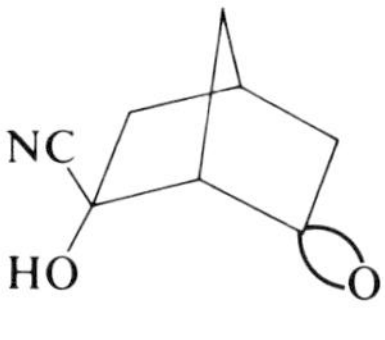

+ HCN → {
(i) *bis*-cyanohydrin products after a short time
(ii) *bis*-cyanohydrin products after a very long time
}

SELECTED REFERENCES

For additional information concerning reaction mechanisms in general the following books are recommended: (a) J. Hine, *Physical Organic Chemistry* (2nd ed.), New York: McGraw-Hill Book Company, 1962; (b) E. S. Gould, *Mechanism and Structure in Organic Chemistry*, New York: Holt, Rinehart & Winston, Inc., 1959; (c) C. K. Ingold, *Structure and Mechanism in Organic Chemistry*, Ithaca, N.Y.: Cornell University Press, 1953. Detailed discussions of certain of the topics covered in this chapter are to be found in (a) W. P. Jencks, "Mechanism and Catalysis of Simple Carbonyl Group Reactions," *Progress in Physical Organic Chemistry*, Vol. 2, New York: Interscience Publishers, Inc., 1964, p. 63; (b) A. V. Kamernitsky and A. A. Akhrem, "The Stereochemistry of Reactions of Nucleophilic Addition to the Carbonyl Group of Cyclic Ketones," *Tetrahedron*, **18**, 705 (1962); (c) M. L. Bender, "Mechanism and Catalysis of Nucleophilic Reactions of Carboxylic Acid Derivatives," *Chem. Rev.*, **60**, 53 (1960); (d) E. L. Eliel, *Stereochemistry of Carbon Compounds*, New York: McGraw-Hill Book Company, 1962.

3

Nucleophilic Addition and Addition-Elimination Reactions with Hetero Atom Nucleophiles and Hydride Ion

3.1 INTRODUCTION

Preparative organic chemistry is not an exact science, but neither is it a strictly empirical art. The organic chemist perceives the landscape of organic reactions with a precision comparable to that of the astronomer viewing the moon through a telescope. The astronomer, on the basis of his observations, can make intelligent guesses concerning the fine details of the moon; the chemist can make intelligent guesses concerning the details of a reaction. But, the astronomer must go to the moon (at least vicariously by means of space vehicles equipped with television cameras) to verify or refute his guesses, and the organic chemist must run the *particular* reaction to verify or refute his predictions. The discussion in this chapter is mainly concerned with the details of reactions of carbonyl compounds as beheld from a distance; it is concerned with setting forth the broad outlines of reactivity, of providing the framework on the basis of which predictions and extrapolations may be made. In any particular case, however, these predictions may not be borne out in quantitative detail, occasionally not even in qualitative detail. Preparative organic chemistry remains an art in the sense that any particular reaction will usually be a little different from its closely related neighbor and will have to be treated in an individual manner. It is this sometimes exasperating aspect which, nevertheless, imbues preparative organic chemistry with

45

that quixotic nature which renders it secure against the inroads of instrumentation and preserves it as a refuge for the artist-chemist [†]

The reader is urged, therefore, to remember that the ideas presented in these chapters are intended as general guide lines, hopefully correct in broad outline but certainly not correct in all specific instances. The present purpose is to instruct in the use of a medium power chemical telescope. When this has been mastered, the fine details can be gained with the more powerful chemical telescopes of the advanced text book, the special monograph, the original literature, or an actual visit with the particular reaction in the laboratory.

Because of the infinite variety made possible by the many nucleophilic agents and carbonyl compounds known to the organic chemist, a comprehensible discussion of these reactions must be fit to some pattern. The one chosen for this book first involves the presentation of those nucleophiles in which the nucleophilic center resides on a hetero atom (Chap. 3) followed then by nucleophiles in which the nucleophilic center resides on carbon (Chap. 4). In each of these two categories, specific examples of direct addition, conjugate addition, and addition-elimination reactions will be cited.

3.2 DIRECT ADDITION OF HETERO ATOM NUCLEOPHILES

Only a few carbonyl compounds (in general, those carrying strongly electron-withdrawing groups close to the carbonyl function) form isolable addition products with nucleophiles containing nitrogen, oxygen, or halogen. Typical examples are the 1-chloro-1-hydroxy derivative from perfluorocyclobutanone, the 2,2-dihydroxy compound from hexafluoroacetone, and the 1-amino-1-hydroxy compound from chloral, as illustrated in Fig. 3-1. In most cases the direct addition of hetero atom nucleo-

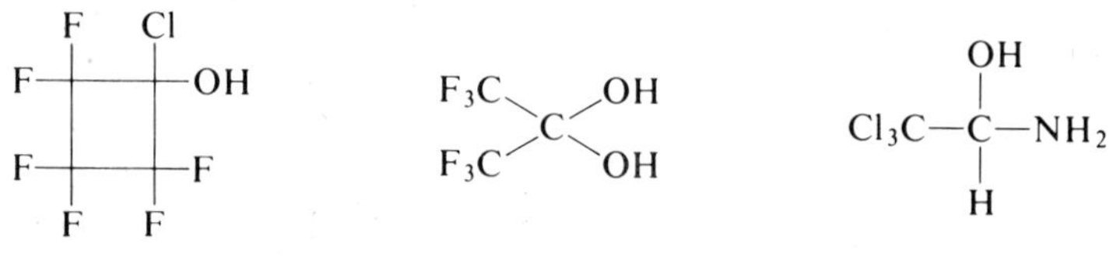

Fig. 3-1 Stable direct addition products from class AA compounds.

philes leads to an isolable product only if followed by an exothermic dehydration along one of the routes illustrated in Fig. 3-2: (a) intermolecular dehydration with a second nucleophilic group; (b) intramolecular dehydration with a proton on the α-carbon; (c) intramolecular dehydration with a proton on the hetero atom.

[†] For an extended discussion of organic synthesis, see R. E. Ireland, *Organic Synthesis* (Englewood Cliffs, N.J.: Prentice-Hall, Inc., in preparation).

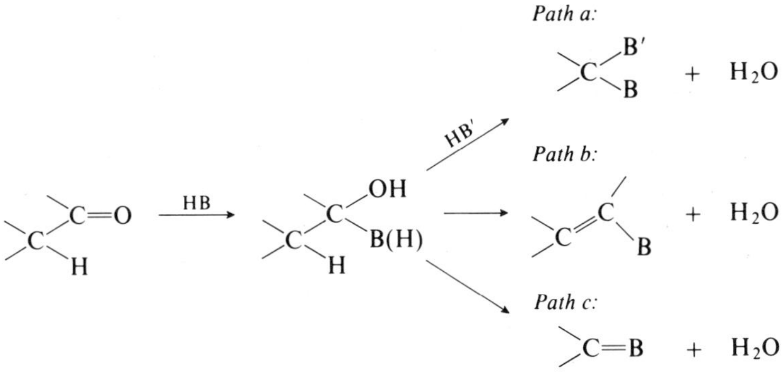

Fig. 3-2 Stable products via direct addition reaction.

Reaction along path *a* is facilitated by acid catalysts in the case of halogen, oxygen, and sulfur nucleophiles, as illustrated in Fig. 3-3. With halide anion as the nucleophile, the reaction provides a method for preparing α-halo ethers ("Henry synthesis"). With alcohols or mercaptans as nucleophiles, it provides a method for making 1,1-dialkoxy compounds (acetals if derived from aldehydes, ketals if derived from ketones) or 1,1-dithioalkoxy compounds (thioacetals and thioketals). Some secondary amines may also react in this fashion to give 1,1-diamino compounds, but the usefulness is limited. Since the initial step in these reactions is a direct carbonyl addition, and since the final product retains the tetrahedral character of the intermediate, the reactions are strongly susceptible to steric influences. This is particularly true of the acetal-forming reaction which is limited, in its simplest applications, to aldehydes and primary alcohols. With secondary or tertiary alcohols, aldehydes are converted to the cor-

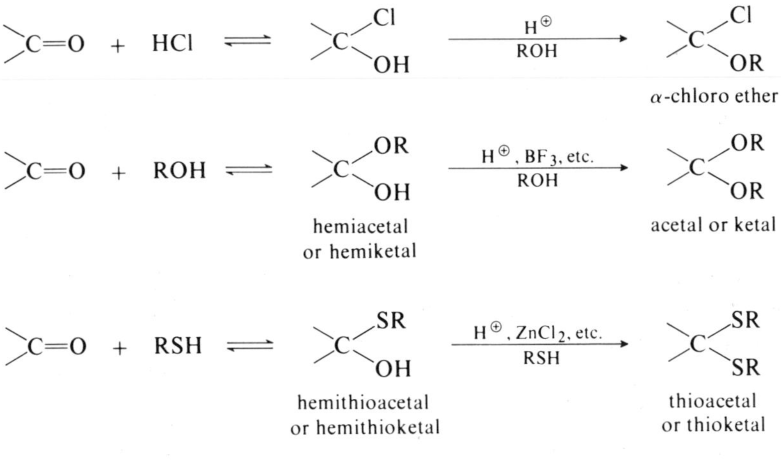

Fig. 3-3 Synthesis of stable carbonyl addition products.

responding acetal only to a limited extent; ketones do not react effectively even with primary alcohols. By the use of ortho esters (e.g., $HC(OC_2H_5)_3$) and acid catalysts, however, ketones can be converted to simple ketals (see problem 4e of Chap. 2). Another device for promoting ketal formation makes use of polyfunctional alcohols, particularly 1,2- or 1,3-dihydroxy compounds. This reaction has been extensively used by the carbohydrate chemist for the protection of hydroxyl groups during interconversions with sugar molecules. For instance, a key step in a synthesis of vitamin C involves selective oxidation of sorbose. To achieve this, all but one of the hydroxyl groups are protected by conversion to a double ketal, as illustrated in Fig. 3-4. The particular usefulness of acetals or ketals for pro-

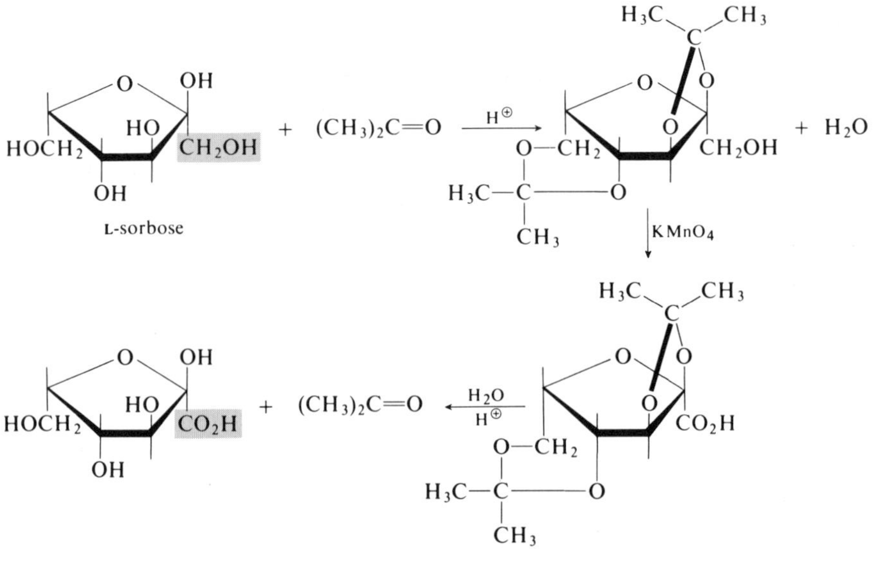

Fig. 3-4 Protection of hydroxyl groups by ketalization.

tecting hydroxyl groups comes from the fact that they are stable to base but easily cleaved by aqueous acid. Thus, the di-ketal derivatives shown in Fig. 3-4 can be converted to the free sugars by treatment with dilute acids. This process may be worked in the other direction as well, and acetals or ketals can be used to protect carbonyl functions as illustrated by the sequence of reactions outlined in Fig. 3-5 (in which the keto group is protected from hydrogenation).

Thioacetals and thioketals form somewhat more readily than acetals and ketals, illustrating the greater nucleophilic character of sulfur. These compounds offer more synthetic possibilities than their oxygen counterparts, for in addition to being convertible back to the carbonyl compound, they can also be oxidized to the corresponding sulfoxides and

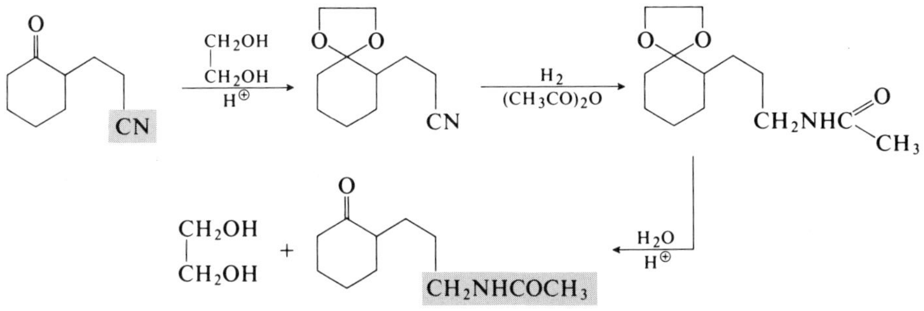

Fig. 3-5 Protection of carbonyl groups by ketalization.

sulfones or reduced (by hydrogen and Raney nickel catalyst) to the hydrocarbons, as illustrated in Fig. 3-6.

Sulfur is a strong enough nucleophile that even in its higher oxidation states it sometimes interacts with carbonyl compounds. Concentrated aqueous solutions of sodium bisulfite form bisulfite addition products

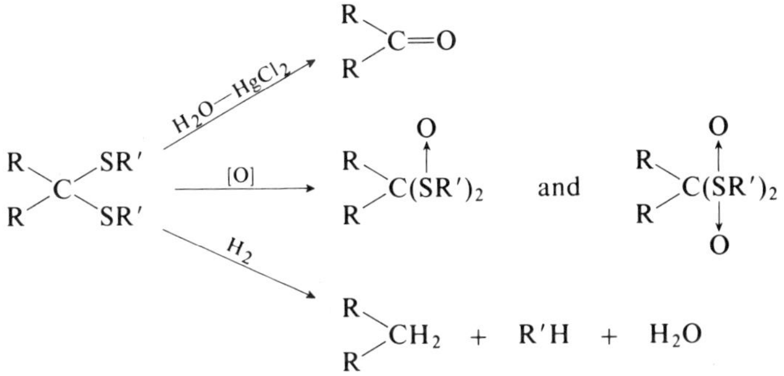

Fig. 3-6 Conversion products from thioacetals or thioketals.

with aldehydes, methyl ketones, and some cyclic ketones. The structure of these compounds, controversial for many years, has been conclusively established to be that shown in Fig. 3-7. The principal utility of bisulfite addition products from class AA compounds is in the purification of mixtures. Most aldehydes and some ketones can be converted to the organic

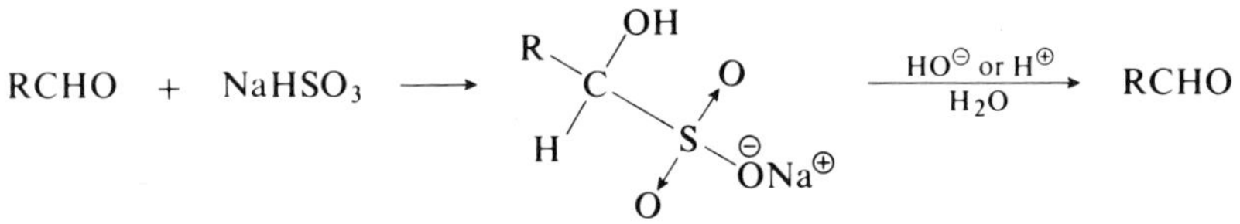

Fig. 3-7 Sodium bisulfite addition products.

solvent-insoluble bisulfite addition products, washed free of materials which do not form adducts, and then reconverted to the parent carbonyl compound by treatment with aqueous acid or base.

Reaction along path *b* of Fig. 3-2 is rarely observed with alcohols or mercaptans but may take place with secondary amines. When cyclohexanone is treated with pyrrolidine in the presence of an acid catalyst, 1-pyrrolidylcyclohexene (an enamine) is formed (see Fig. 3-8). Enamines are useful intermediates in certain types of C-alkylation reactions (see Fig. 5-11).

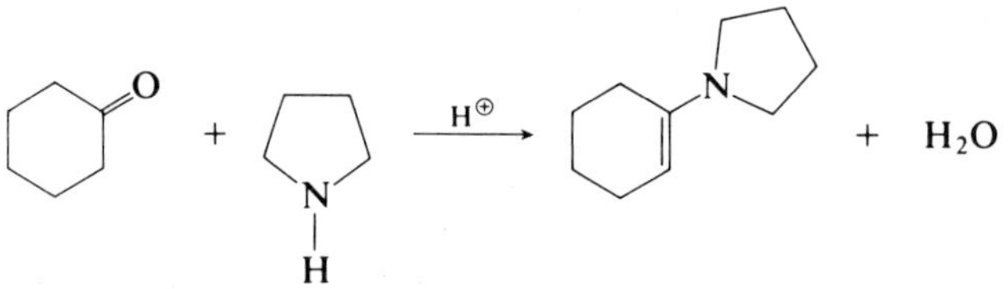

Fig. 3-8 Formation of enamine of cyclohexanone.

Reaction along path *c* of Fig. 3-2 is characteristic of primary amines (and ammonia). Numerous compounds of the general structure H_2N—R can be used where R may be an aliphatic group (aliphatic amines), an aromatic group (aromatic amines), an amino group (hydrazine), an NHAr group (aryl hydrazine), an OH group (hydroxylamine), an $NHCONH_2$ group (semicarbazide), etc. The products resulting from these several possibilities are shown in Fig. 3-9. The most frequent use to which these products are put is in the characterization of aldehydes and ketones.

Amine Component:	*Product:*	*Class of Product:*
RNH_2	$R_2C{=}NR$	imine or Shiff's base
NH_2NH_2	$R_2C{=}NNH_2$	hydrazone
	or $R_2C{=}NN{=}CR_2$	azine
$C_6H_5NHNH_2$	$R_2C{=}NNHC_6H_5$	phenylhydrazone
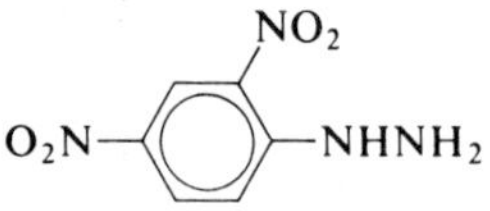	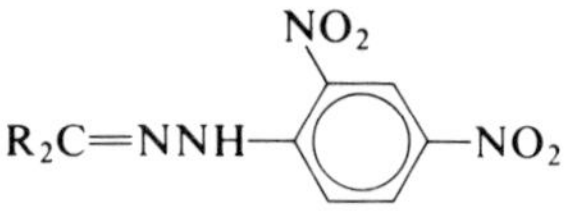	2,4-dinitrophenylhydrazone
$NH_2NHCONH_2$	$R_2C{=}NNHCONH_2$	semicarbazone
NH_2OH	$R_2C{=}NOH$	oxime

Fig. 3-9 Amine derivatives of aldehydes and ketones.

Many of these compounds, particularly those derived from hydrazine-based amine components, are crystalline, high-melting solids which are readily purified by crystallization. For instance, benzaldehyde melts at $-26°C$ (i.e., is liquid at room temperature), while the corresponding 2,4-dinitrophenylhydrazone melts at 237°C. Not only do these compounds provide ideal derivatives for characterization, but they also provide a means for separating a particular aldehyde or ketone from a mixture. The carbonyl derivatives can be reconverted to the parent carbonyl compound either by acid-catalyzed hydrolysis or by acid-catalyzed carbonyl interchange. The latter method, illustrated in Fig. 3-10, uses compounds such as pyruvic acid, which are activated by adjacent electron-withdrawing groups.

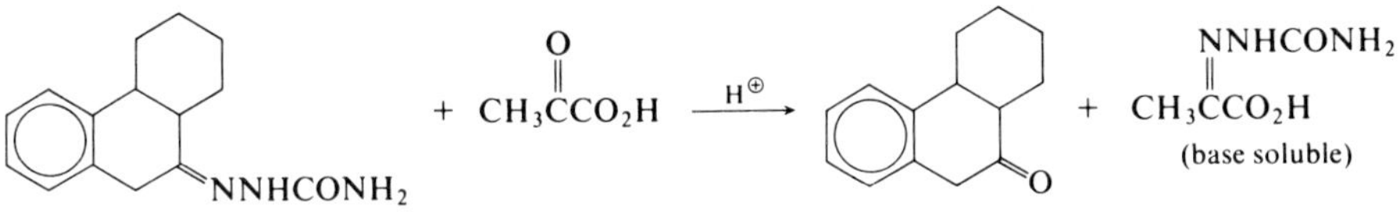

Fig. 3-10 Regeneration of carbonyl compounds by carbonyl interchange.

A more elegant purification method via imine derivatives employs compounds of the structure $R_3\overset{\oplus}{N}CH_2CONHNH_2$ ("Girard's reagents"). The products from Girard's reagents and aldehydes or ketones are, by virtue of the quaternary ammonium grouping, soluble in water and hence readily separated from water-insoluble contaminants. Reconversion to the parent aldehyde or ketone can be effected by the methods already mentioned. This procedure has been particularly useful in the isolation and purification of naturally occurring aldehydes and ketones, as illustrated in Fig. 3-11.

Phenylhydrazine has been an extremely important reagent in sugar chemistry,[†] for it reacts with aldoses and ketoses to form phenylhydra-

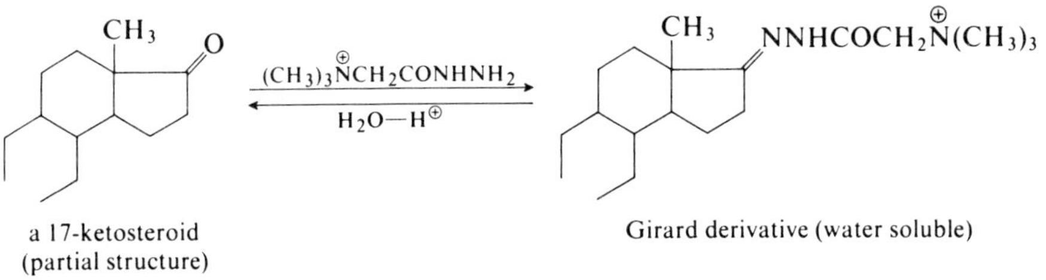

a 17-ketosteroid
(partial structure)

Girard derivative (water soluble)

Fig. 3-11 Purification of carbonyl compounds via Girard's reagent.

† See R. L. Barker, *Organic Chemistry of Biological Compounds* (Englewood Cliffs, N.J.: Prentice-Hall, Inc., in preparation).

zones. With an excess of phenylhydrazine, however, an oxidation takes place at the position adjacent to the carbonyl group, and a *bis*-phenyl-hydrazone (an osazone) is produced. This reaction, characteristic of α-hydroxy aldehydes and α-hydroxy ketones in general, is illustrated in Fig. 3-12 with the sugar D-glucose. Sugar osazones are excellent characterization derivatives in being crystallizable, high-melting compounds. They may also be useful in destroying asymmetry at the position adjacent to the carbonyl group of a sugar (as in glucose; see Fig. 3-12) thus allowing certain stereochemical relationships between sugars to be more easily discerned.

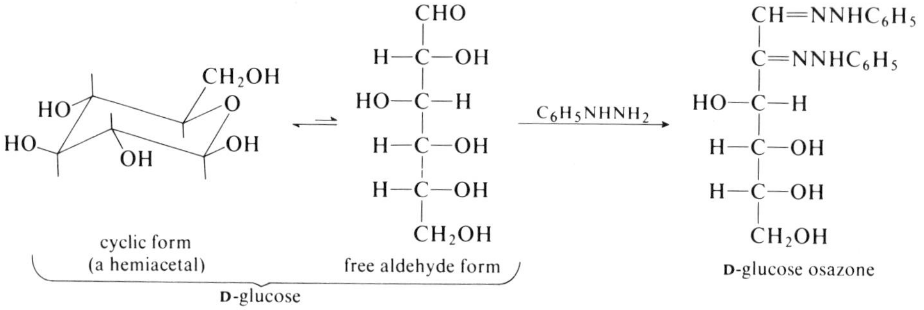

Fig. 3-12 Osazone formation from D-glucose.

With ammonia as the amine component, the initially formed dehydration product is an imine of the structure $R_2C=NH$. These are very unstable compounds which either polymerize or react with additional ammonia and carbonyl compounds. For instance, six molecules of formaldehyde react with four molecules of ammonia to form the highly symmetrical compound hexamethylenetetramine (also called hexamine or urotropin); three molecules of benzaldehyde and two molecules of ammonia react to form a product which, at least in a formal sense, may be considered as the monomeric structure of which hexamethylenetetramine is a dimeric type (Fig. 3-13).

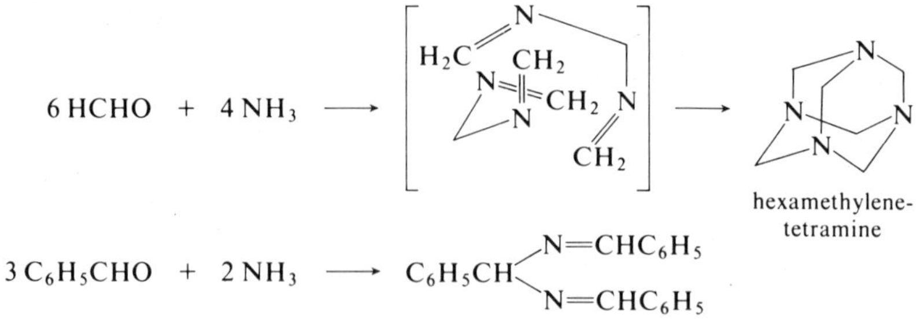

Fig. 3-13 Products from ammonia and aldehydes.

Direct addition reactions of class D carbonyl compounds lead to stable products, because the initially formed intermediates are enol species. With few exceptions, enols are unstable and quickly tautomerize to the more stable carbonyl form, thus driving the reaction to completion. Hetero atom nucleophiles containing one or more hydrogen atoms attached to the nucleophilic center readily react with ketenes and isocyanates to furnish products of the types illustrated in Fig. 3-14.

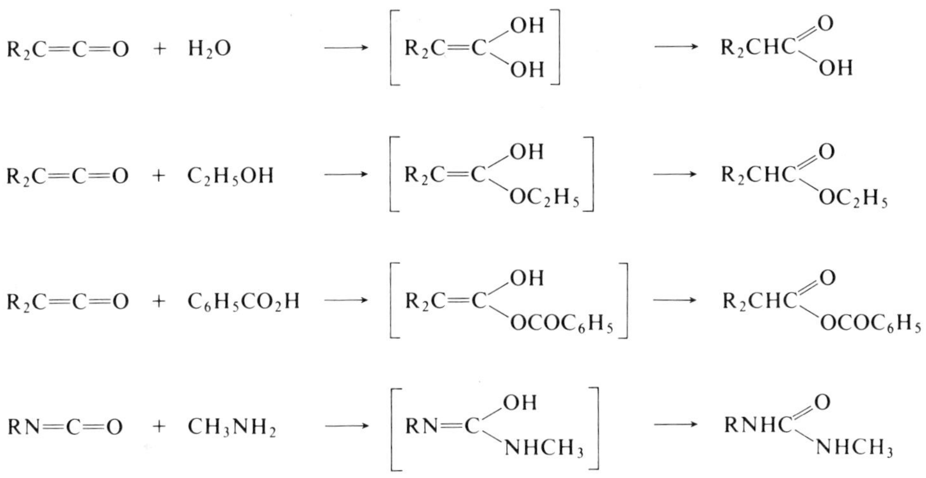

$$R_2C{=}C{=}O \ + \ H_2O \longrightarrow \left[R_2C{=}C\overset{\textstyle OH}{\underset{\textstyle OH}{\Big\langle}} \right] \longrightarrow R_2CHC\overset{\textstyle O}{\underset{\textstyle OH}{\Big\langle}}$$

$$R_2C{=}C{=}O \ + \ C_2H_5OH \longrightarrow \left[R_2C{=}C\overset{\textstyle OH}{\underset{\textstyle OC_2H_5}{\Big\langle}} \right] \longrightarrow R_2CHC\overset{\textstyle O}{\underset{\textstyle OC_2H_5}{\Big\langle}}$$

$$R_2C{=}C{=}O \ + \ C_6H_5CO_2H \longrightarrow \left[R_2C{=}C\overset{\textstyle OH}{\underset{\textstyle OCOC_6H_5}{\Big\langle}} \right] \longrightarrow R_2CHC\overset{\textstyle O}{\underset{\textstyle OCOC_6H_5}{\Big\langle}}$$

$$RN{=}C{=}O \ + \ CH_3NH_2 \longrightarrow \left[RN{=}C\overset{\textstyle OH}{\underset{\textstyle NHCH_3}{\Big\langle}} \right] \longrightarrow RNHC\overset{\textstyle O}{\underset{\textstyle NHCH_3}{\Big\langle}}$$

Fig. 3-14 Reaction of hetero atom nucleophiles with class D compounds.

Ketene itself ($CH_2{=}C{=}O$), available by pyrolysis of acetone at 700–750°C, provides a commercial starting material for acetic anhydride. Ketene readily forms a dimer which can be converted back to the monomer by heating or can be used as a reactant in its own right as, for instance, in the commercial preparation of acetoacetic ester (see Fig. 3-15).

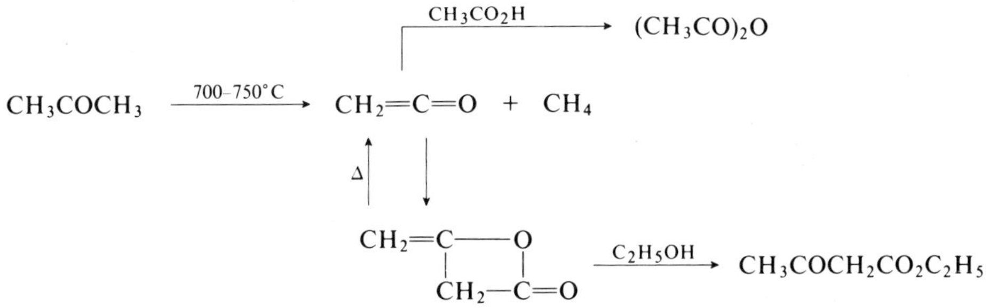

$$CH_3COCH_3 \xrightarrow{700-750°C} CH_2{=}C{=}O \ + \ CH_4$$

$$\xrightarrow[\quad]{CH_3CO_2H} (CH_3CO)_2O$$

$$CH_2{=}C{-}O \atop CH_2{-}C{=}O \xrightarrow{C_2H_5OH} CH_3COCH_2CO_2C_2H_5$$

Fig. 3-15 Preparation and reactions of ketene.

3.3 CONJUGATE ADDITION OF HETERO ATOM NUCLEOPHILES

Conjugate addition is generally less reversible than direct addition, and as a result, nucleophiles which give unstable direct addition products frequently lead to stable conjugate addition products. For example, hydrogen chloride reacts with quinones in a fashion comparable to that of the much more nucleophilic amines to give conjugate addition products, as illustrated by examples *a* and *b* in Fig. 3-16. The ease with which a hetero atom nucleophile adds in conjugate fashion increases from halogen to oxygen (to sulfur) to nitrogen. Conjugate addition of oxygen-containing nucleophiles is largely confined to alcohols which, under the influence of acid or base, add to α,β-unsaturated carbonyl compounds as illustrated

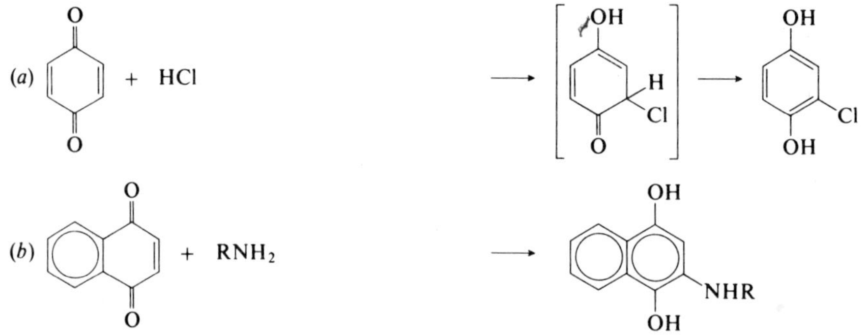

(a) [quinone] + HCl →

(b) [naphthoquinone] + RNH$_2$ →

(c) $CH_3CH{=}CHCHO$ + C_2H_5OH (excess) $\xrightarrow{H^\oplus}$ $CH_3CHCH_2CH(OC_2H_5)_2$ with OC_2H_5

(d) $CH_2{=}CHCO_2C_2H_5$ + ROH $\xrightarrow{RONa}$ $ROCH_2CH_2CO_2C_2H_5$

(e)† $CH_2{=}CHCN$ + $HOCH_2CH_2SH$ → $HOCH_2CH_2SCH_2CH_2CN$

(f) $CH_2{=}CHCO_2C_2H_5$ + $\begin{array}{c}HOCH_2CH_2\\HOCH_2CH_2\end{array}NH$ → $\begin{array}{c}HOCH_2CH_2\\HOCH_2CH_2\end{array}N{-}CH_2CH_2CO_2C_2H_5$

(g) $C_6H_5CH{=}CHCOC_6H_5$ + $NaHSO_3$ → $C_6H_5CHCH_2COC_6H_5$ with SO_3Na

(h) $CH_2{=}CHCO_2C_2H_5$ + CH_3NH_2 (excess) → $CH_3N\begin{array}{c}CH_2CH_2CO_2C_2H_5\\CH_2CH_2CO_2C_2H_5\end{array}$

(i) $(CH_3)_2C{=}CHCOCH_3$ + NH_3 (excess) → $(CH_3)_2CCH_2COCH_3$ with NH_2

Fig. 3-16 Conjugate additions with hetero atom nucleophiles.

† The carbonyl group is but one of several functions that can promote conjugate addition. Other electron-withdrawing groups including NO_2, SO_2R, and CN also suffice as, for instance, in this example.

by examples *c* and *d* of Fig. 3-16; in some cases (e.g., example *c*), both modes of addition are observed. Sulfur and nitrogen are more nucleophilic than oxygen, as illustrated by examples *e* and *f* of Fig. 3-16 in which bifunctional molecules are involved. Even bisulfite is capable of adding in a conjugate fashion, as illustrated by example *g* of Fig. 3-16. All of the hydrogens attached to the hetero atom nucleophilic center have the potentiality of being replaced by the moiety derived from the α,β-unsaturated carbonyl compound, and in the presence of excess of the latter this may be achieved (example *h* of Fig. 3-16); conversely, by limiting the amount of α,β-unsaturated carbonyl compound, the reaction can be restricted to mono addition (example *i* in Fig. 3-16).

3.4 ADDITION-ELIMINATION OF HETERO ATOM NUCLEOPHILES

The characteristic reaction of carbonyl functions carrying type C groups is nucleophilic addition-elimination (although conjugate addition is an alternative process if the carbonyl function also carries a type B group). The "-olysis reactions" (including hydrolysis, alcoholysis, acidolysis, and aminolysis) take place with increasing ease as the anionic stability of the type C group increases. Thus, acid halides hydrolyze most readily, acid anhydrides hydrolyze somewhat less readily, esters hydrolyze under moderately strenuous conditions, and amides hydrolyze only under quite strenuous conditions. Acid halides, then, are the most generally applicable reagents for the preparation of anhydrides, esters, and amides. Standing at the top of this energy ladder, they cannot be prepared by "-olysis reactions" from members on the lower rungs of this ladder and require other methods of synthesis. Usually, acid chlorides are made by the action of thionyl chloride, phosphorus trichloride, or phosphorus pentachloride on carboxylic acids. The reagent of choice in any particular case is the one which allows the cleanest separation of product, as illustrated by the specific examples in Fig. 3-17 (note relative boiling points of

$$CH_3CH_2CO_2H \quad + \quad PCl_3 \quad \longrightarrow \quad CH_3CH_2COCl \quad + \quad H_3PO_4$$

b.p. 180°   b.p. 80°   dec. 200°

subl. 162°   b.p. 304°   b.p. 107°

b.p. 77°   b.p. 184°

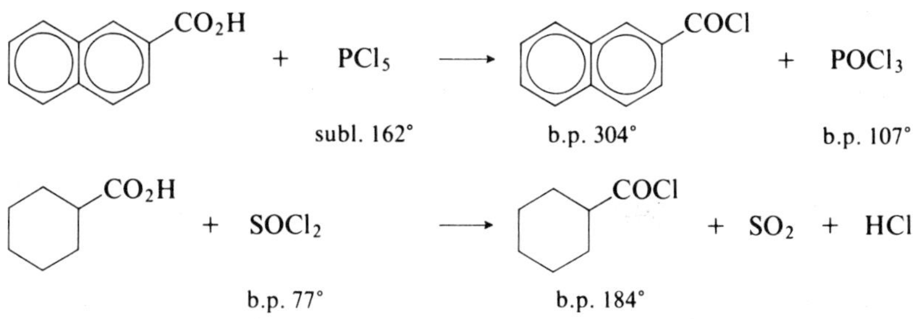

Fig. 3-17 Preparation of acid chlorides.

reactants and products). These reactions can be considered as the acyl analogs of the conversion of alcohols to alkyl chlorides with these same reagents.†

Anhydrides are frequently used in place of acid halides for the preparation of esters and amides, particularly for the synthesis of acetyl compounds via acetic anhydride. A special application of anhydrides involves the alcoholysis of cyclic members which, in the absence of an acid catalyst, lead to half esters. In the presence of an acid catalyst the full ester is formed as the result of an alcoholysis followed by an acid-catalyzed esterification. Several typical examples of "-olysis reactions" are shown in Fig. 3-18.

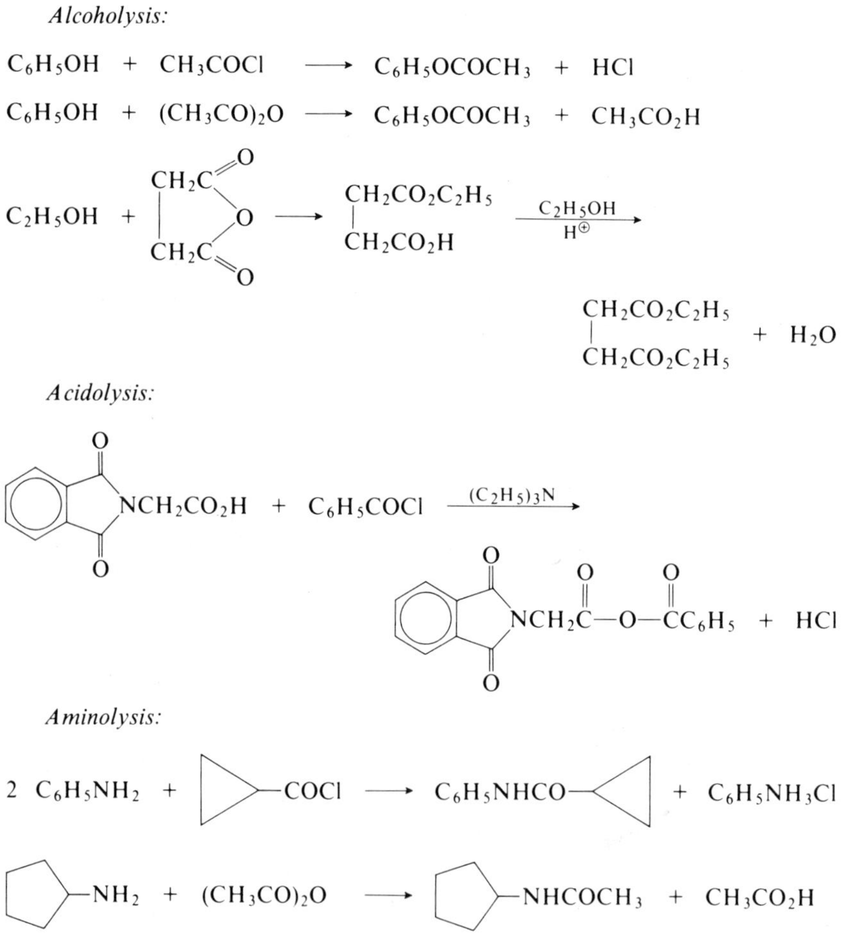
Alcoholysis:
C6H5OH + CH3COCl → C6H5OCOCH3 + HCl
C6H5OH + (CH3CO)2O → C6H5OCOCH3 + CH3CO2H
C2H5OH
CH2CO2C2H5
CH2CO2H
C2H5OH
H⊕
CH2CO2C2H5
CH2CO2C2H5
+ H2O
Acidolysis:
NCH2CO2H + C6H5COCl
(C2H5)3N
NCH2C—O—CC6H5 + HCl
Aminolysis:
2 C6H5NH2 +
COCl
C6H5NHCO
+ C6H5NH3Cl
NH2 + (CH3CO)2O
NHCOCH3 + CH3CO2H

Fig. 3-18 "-Olysis reactions" of acid chlorides and acid anhydrides.

† W. H. Saunders, Jr., *op. cit.*

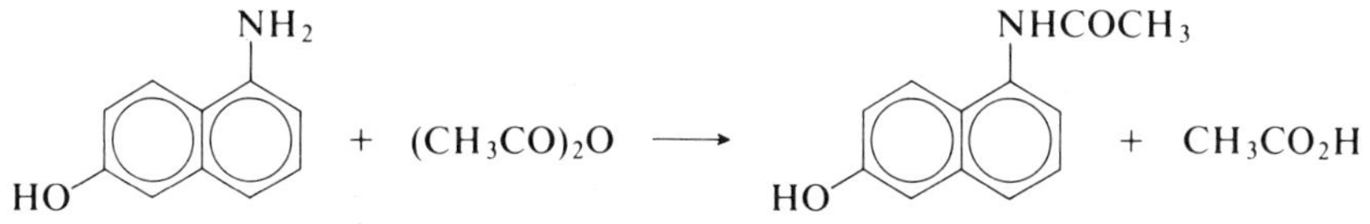
NH2
HO
+ (CH3CO)2O
NHCOCH3
HO
+ CH3CO2H

Fig. 3-19 Selective acetylation of a polyfunctional nucleophile.

Nitrogen is a better nucleophilic center than oxygen, and selective addition-elimination may sometimes be accomplished as, for instance, in the acetylation of 1-amino-6-hydroxynaphthalene (Fig. 3-19).

The alkoxyl group is a better "leaving group" than the amido group (i.e., ROH is a stronger acid than R_2NH), and amides and derivatives can be prepared by aminolysis of esters as illustrated in Fig. 3-20.

The equilibrium constants for the "-olysis reactions" which have been discussed to this point are large enough that the product is obtained in high yield without recourse to special methods. Certain other "-olysis reactions," however, involve equilibria which are less favorable and which require special methods of product removal to be driven to completion. A good example is the acid-catalyzed addition of alcohols to carboxylic acids (esterification-hydrolysis equilibrium). Since the acidities of HOH and ROH are comparable (in contrast with acidities of HCl and ROH in alcoholysis of acid chlorides), the tetrahedral intermediate decomposes in either direction, i.e., to carboxylic acid (hydrolysis route) or to the carboxylic ester (alcoholysis route), and the system possesses an equilibrium constant close to unity (in contrast with the equilibrium constant for the alcoholysis of acid chloride which is much greater than 1). One way in which the equilibrium can be shifted to favor ester formation is to increase the concentration of the carboxylic acid or the alcohol. A standard method for the preparation of the esters from simple alcohols such as ethanol, for instance, involves the refluxing of one mole equivalent of the acid with a large excess (5–10 molar) of alcohol in the presence of a small amount of

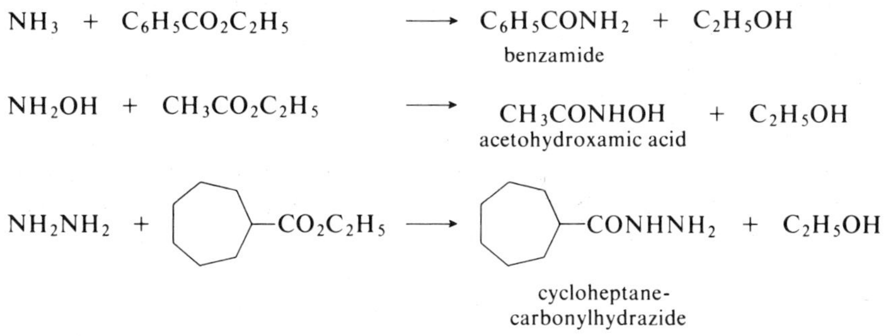
NH3 + C6H5CO2C2H5 → C6H5CONH2 + C2H5OH
benzamide
NH2OH + CH3CO2C2H5 → CH3CONHOH + C2H5OH
acetohydroxamic acid
NH2NH2 +
CO2C2H5
CONHNH2 + C2H5OH
cycloheptane-
carbonylhydrazide

Fig. 3-20 Aminolysis of esters.

sulfuric acid. A more effective way for pushing the reaction in the direction of ester formation involves the removal of water as it forms. Ethyl esters, for instance, can be produced in almost quantitative yield by carrying out the reaction in a mixture of benzene and ethanol containing a small amount of sulfuric acid. Distilling out of the refluxing mixture is a ternary azeotrope of water, alcohol, and benzene which separates into two layers upon condensation, the lower layer consisting of alcohol and water, and the upper layer of alcohol and benzene. By means of the apparatus pictured in Fig. 3-21, the lower layer can be drawn off, and the upper layer returned to the reaction mixture. Water removal by azeotrope formation

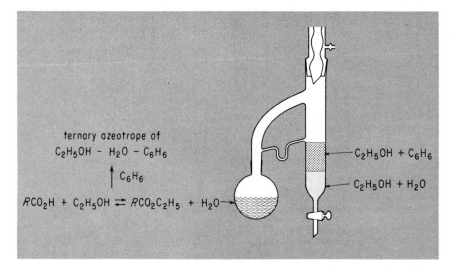

ternary azeotrope of
$$C_2H_5OH - H_2O - C_6H_6$$

$\uparrow C_6H_6$

$$RCO_2H + C_2H_5OH \rightleftarrows RCO_2C_2H_5 + H_2O \rightarrow$$

$C_2H_5OH + C_6H_6$

$C_2H_5OH + H_2O$

Fig. 3-21 Preparation of esters by azeotropic water removal.

represents a device that is applicable not only in esterification reactions but in many other instances as well. For instance, the formation of acetals and ketals, of thioacetals and thioketals, and of enamines (see Sec. 3.2) are examples of reactions where this technique has been applied. Still another method for water removal in esterification reactions, particularly applicable to the preparation of methyl esters, makes use of 2,2-dimethoxypropane (i.e., the dimethyl ketal of acetone). This compound undergoes hydrolysis under acidic conditions in an essentially irreversible reaction to yield acetone and methanol (see p. 48); thus, water is effectively removed as it forms, and the esterification proceeds to completion.

Just as an excess of alcohol displaces the equilibrium in the carboxylic acid-alcohol system in the direction of ester formation, so an excess of water displaces the equilibrium in the direction of carboxylic acid formation. Acid-catalyzed hydrolysis is carried out simply by treating the ester with aqueous acid. Even more complete hydrolysis can be effected, how-ever, under basic conditions. This is due to the conversion of the car-boxylic acid to the carboxylate ion, an essentially irreversible process which thereby removes one of the members from the equilibrium system, as illustrated in Fig. 3-22.

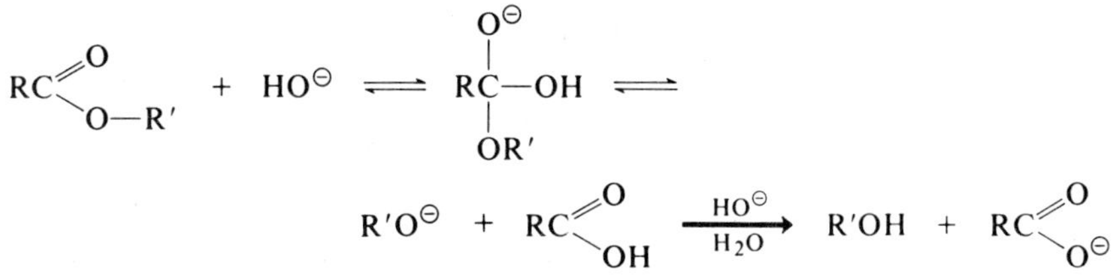

$$RC\overset{O}{\underset{O-R'}{\diagup}} \;+\; HO^{\ominus} \;\rightleftharpoons\; RC\overset{O^{\ominus}}{\underset{OR'}{-}}OH \;\rightleftharpoons$$

$$R'O^{\ominus} \;+\; RC\overset{O}{\underset{OH}{\diagup}} \;\xrightarrow[H_2O]{HO^{\ominus}}\; R'OH \;+\; RC\overset{O}{\underset{O^{\ominus}}{\diagup}}$$

Fig. 3-22 Base-induced hydrolysis of esters.

Both the acid- and base-induced hydrolyses of amides may go virtually to completion. In the base-induced reaction the carboxylate anion is formed (see discussion of ester hydrolysis), and in the acid-induced reac-tion the ammonium cation is formed. Since the latter has no nucleophilic character, the reversion to the tetrahedral intermediate cannot take place, and the reaction is essentially irreversible, as illustrated in Fig. 3-23.

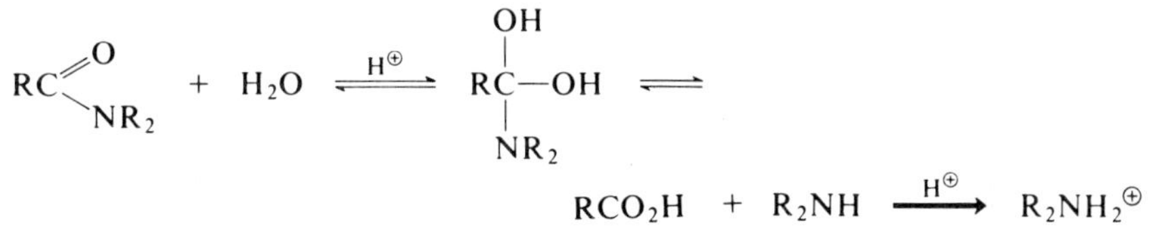

$$RC\overset{O}{\underset{NR_2}{\diagup}} \;+\; H_2O \;\underset{H^{\oplus}}{\rightleftharpoons}\; RC\overset{OH}{\underset{NR_2}{-}}OH \;\rightleftharpoons$$

$$RCO_2H \;+\; R_2NH \;\xrightarrow{H^{\oplus}}\; R_2NH_2^{\oplus}$$

Fig. 3-23 Acid-induced hydrolysis of amides.

The alcoholysis of esters, referred to as ester interchange, is carried out by mixing an ester and an alcohol in the presence of either an acid or a base catalyst. The reaction is useful only if the equilibrium constant is considerably different from unity (not the usual case) or if one of the con-stituents of the equilibrium mixture can be selectively removed. For in-stance, ethyl acetoacetate, when heated with *n*-octyl alcohol and a trace of sodium (ROH + Na → RONa + H_2), establishes an equilibrium mix-ture containing the starting materials, along with *n*-octyl acetoacetate and ethanol. If the temperature of the mixture is maintained above the boiling point of ethanol (b.p. 78°) but below the boiling points of the other three constituents, the ethanol can be boiled out and *n*-octyl aceto-acetate obtained in high yield. This example (see Fig. 3-24) illustrates

$$CH_3COCH_2CO_2C_2H_5 \; + \; C_8H_{17}OH \; \rightleftharpoons \; CH_3COCH_2CO_2C_8H_{17} \; + \; C_2H_5OH$$

Fig. 3-24 Ester interchange with acetoacetic ester.

one aspect of the special usefulness of the ester interchange method; to prepare octyl acetoacetate via the free acid would be exceedingly difficult because of the great tendency of acetoacetic acid (and β-keto acids in general) to decarboxylate (see Fig. 5-17). The preparation of benzyl esters by ester interchange illustrates another application. Benzyl esters are useful in that they can be cleaved by hydrogenolysis (e.g., $RCO_2CH_2C_6H_5$ + H_2 (Pd-C) $\rightarrow$ RCO_2H + $C_6H_5CH_3$). Thus, they afford a good means for protecting a carboxyl group during a series of reactions, after which the free carboxyl group can be liberated by a nonhydrolysis step (thereby preserving any other hydrolyzable groups in the molecule).

A number of other interchange reactions involving carboxylic acid derivatives and nucleophilic species are possible, including acid halide-hydrogen halide interchange, carboxylic anhydride-carboxylic acid interchange, ester-carboxylic acid interchange, etc., as illustrated in Fig. 3-25.

$$RCOCl \; + \; HX \qquad \rightleftharpoons \; RCOX \; + \; HCl$$

$$RCO_2H \; + \; (R'CO)_2O \; \rightleftharpoons \; R'CO_2H \; + \; (RCO)_2O$$

$$RCO_2C_2H_5 \; + \; R'CO_2H \; \rightleftharpoons \; R'CO_2C_2H_5 \; + \; RCO_2H$$

Fig. 3-25 Interchange reactions with class AC compounds.

The addition-elimination reaction is generally restricted to class AC, BC, and CC compounds. However, if a class AA compound carries a group which can exist as a stable carbanion, addition-elimination may be observed in this series also (see Fig. 2-17 for mechanism). For example, when compounds of the general structure $RCOCH_3$ (or convertible to $RCOCH_3$ by oxidation, e.g., $RCHOHCH_3$) are treated with strongly alkaline solutions containing chlorine, bromine, or iodine, the initially-formed trihalo ketone ($RCOCX_3$) undergoes an addition-elimination reaction to give carboxylate anion and haloform (CHX_3). The overall process, referred to as the "haloform reaction," is useful as a preparative method for carboxylic acids and as a diagnostic tool in structure elucidation. For the latter purpose, iodine is most often used as the halogen component, in which case the products are the carboxylic acid and iodoform (CHI_3). Iodoform appears in the reaction mixture as a flocculent, pale yellow precipitate which possesses a very characteristic odor; by this means, then, one can "smell" the presence of a $-COCH_3$ group (i.e., a methyl ketone) or a $-CH(OH)CH_3$ group (i.e., ethanol, a methyl alkyl carbinol, or a methyl aryl carbinol) in an organic compound,

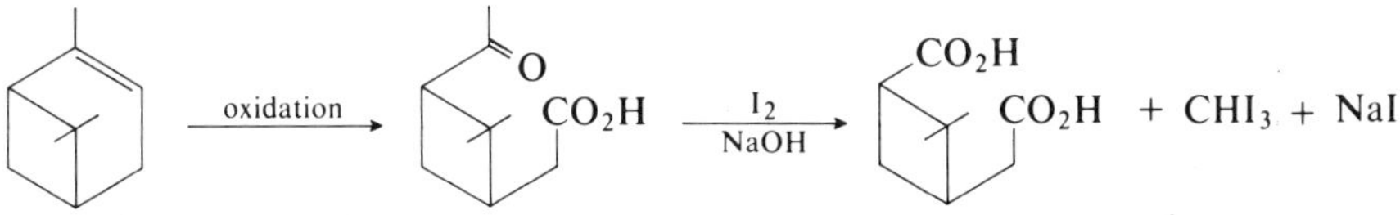

pinene
(a natural product)

$$CH_3(CH_2)_5CH\begin{smallmatrix}OH\\CH_3\end{smallmatrix} + I_2 + NaOH \longrightarrow CH_3(CH_2)_5CO_2H + CHI_3 + NaI$$

Fig. 3-26 Iodoform reaction.

as illustrated in Fig. 3-26. The nose, however, is not an infallible guide, and it is a wise precaution to actually isolate the iodoform and insure that it has the correct melting point of 119°.

β-Dicarbonyl compounds represent another group of class AA compounds susceptible to addition-elimination. An interesting and important example is acetoacetic ester, which has both an AA type carbonyl and an AC type carbonyl. In the presence of dilute acid or dilute base, acetoacetic esters undergo addition-elimination at the ester group and yield the corresponding acetoacetic acids (easily decarboxylated). With more concentrated base, however, the reaction takes a different course and leads to cleavage between the α and β carbon atoms. These two modes of decomposition are sometimes referred to as the "ketone cleavage" (i.e., the product is a ketone) and the "acid cleavage" (i.e., the product is a carboxylic acid) and are illustrated in Fig. 3-27. Why the "acid cleavage

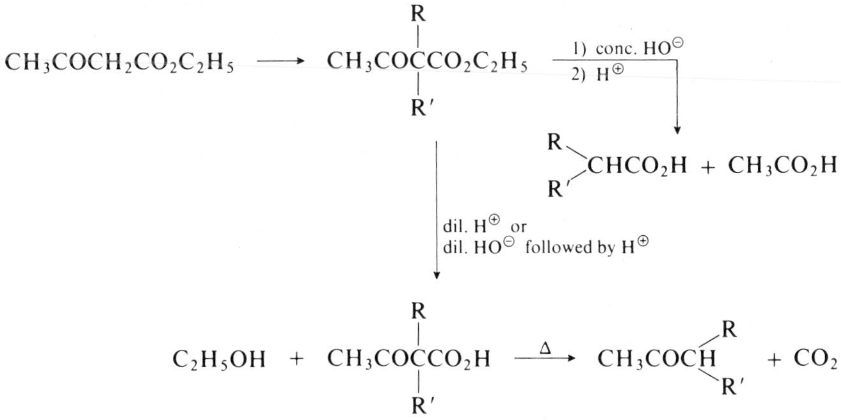

Fig. 3-27 Synthesis of substituted acetic acids and substituted acetones via acetoacetic ester.

route" is preferred over the "ketone cleavage route" as the hydroxide ion concentration increases is not entirely clear, but it may involve the formation of dianions as reactive intermediates. Because various groups can be introduced into the active methylene positions of acetoacetic ester (see Sec. 5.3), it is an important synthesis intermediate in the preparation of substituted acetic acids (acid cleavage) and substituted acetones (ketone cleavage).

An example of a type Z addition-elimination (see Fig. 2-18) involving a hetero atom nucleophile is the action of peracids on ketones. Perbenzoic acid, for instance, reacts with ketones in the fashion illustrated by the sequence shown in Fig. 3-28. The initial step is an acid-catalyzed carbonyl addition to yield a tetrahedral intermediate which subsequently undergoes acid-catalyzed decomposition along path *b* of Fig. 2-18 because of the good "leaving ability" of the protonated benzoate moiety (i.e., benzoic acid is a stable compound).

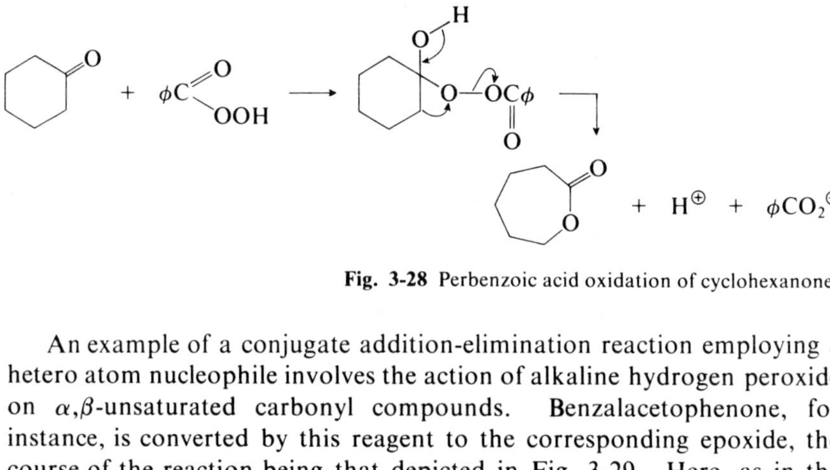

Fig. 3-28 Perbenzoic acid oxidation of cyclohexanone.

An example of a conjugate addition-elimination reaction employing a hetero atom nucleophile involves the action of alkaline hydrogen peroxide on α,β-unsaturated carbonyl compounds. Benzalacetophenone, for instance, is converted by this reagent to the corresponding epoxide, the course of the reaction being that depicted in Fig. 3-29. Here, as in the preceding case, the termination step is the result of the nucleophilic reagent having carried into the adduct a group which can be expelled as a stable entity, in this instance the hydroxyl anion.

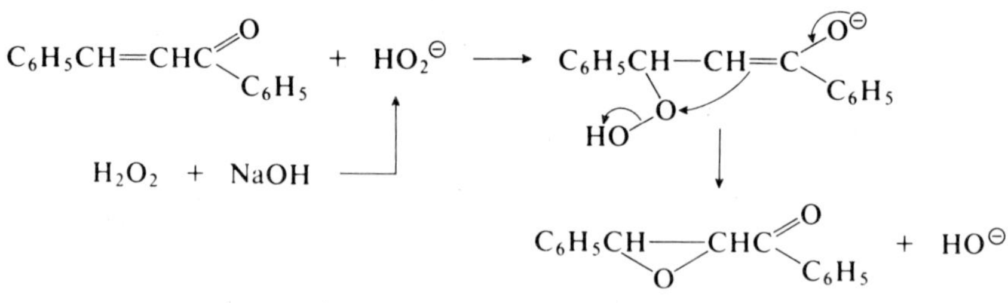

Fig. 3-29 Epoxidation of benzalacetophenone with alkaline peroxide.

3.5 HYDRIDE ION AS A NUCLEOPHILE

A variety of metal hydrides, such as lithium aluminum hydride and sodium borohydride, have become available to the organic chemist over the last two decades. These have provided him with a powerful means for effecting reductions of carbonyl groups in a chemically-selective and stereochemically-selective fashion.[†] Although the metal atoms of the hydride reducing agents may interact with carbonyl compounds by coordinating with the oxygen, the reaction of significance is the transfer of a hydrogen anion (hydride ion) from the metal hydride to the carbonyl carbon atom, as depicted in Fig. 3-30. The "nucleophilic potential" of the

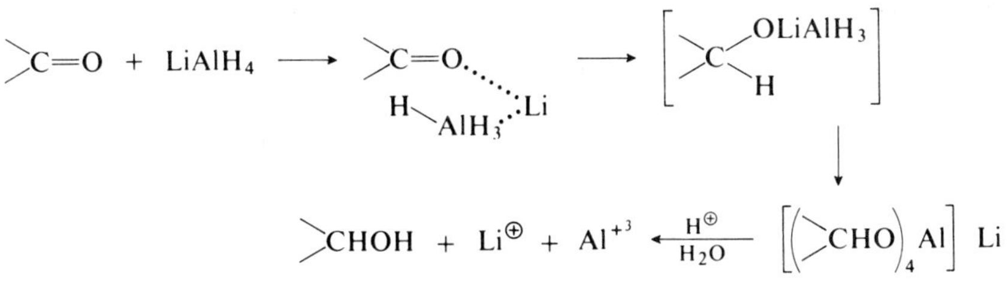

$$\text{>C=O} + \text{LiAlH}_4 \longrightarrow \text{>C=O} \overset{}{\underset{H \diagdown \text{AlH}_3}{\cdots}} \text{:Li} \longrightarrow \left[\text{>C} \overset{\text{OLiAlH}_3}{\underset{H}{\diagup}} \right]$$

$$\text{>CHOH} + \text{Li}^{\oplus} + \text{Al}^{+3} \xleftarrow[\text{H}_2\text{O}]{\text{H}^{\oplus}} \left[\left(\text{>CHO} \right)_4 \text{Al} \right] \text{Li}$$

Fig. 3-30 Lithium aluminum hydride reduction of carbonyl compounds.

hydride ion depends on the particular hydride reagent employed. Lithium aluminum hydride, for example, is a particularly potent hydride donor and is capable of reducing carboxyl groups (a notoriously difficult process by most other means) and almost all other types of carbonyl groups (Fig. 3-31). Sodium borohydride, on the other hand, is much milder in its

Primary Alcohol Syntheses:

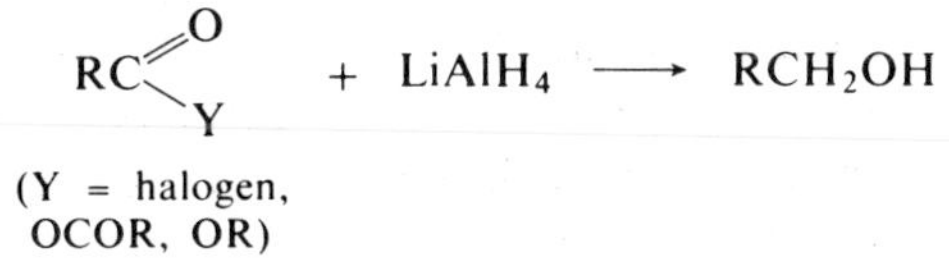

$$\text{RC} \overset{\diagup \text{O}}{\underset{\diagdown \text{Y}}{}} + \text{LiAlH}_4 \longrightarrow \text{RCH}_2\text{OH}$$

(Y = halogen,
OCOR, OR)

Primary, Secondary, and Tertiary Amine Syntheses:

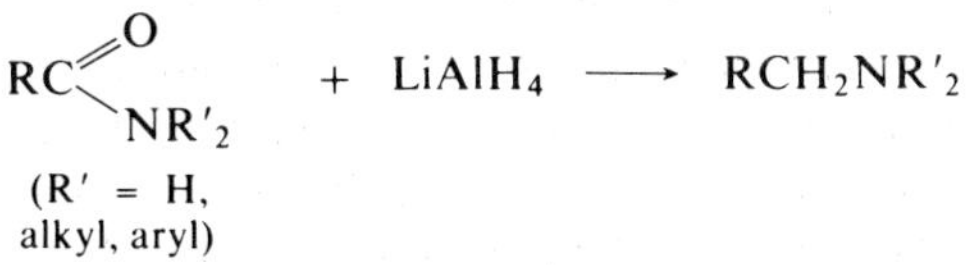

$$\text{RC} \overset{\diagup \text{O}}{\underset{\diagdown \text{NR}'_2}{}} + \text{LiAlH}_4 \longrightarrow \text{RCH}_2\text{NR}'_2$$

(R' = H,
alkyl, aryl)

Fig. 3-31 Lithium aluminum hydride reduction of carboxylic acids and derivatives.

[†] For an expanded discussion of the reduction of carbonyl compounds, see K. L. Rinehart, Jr., *Oxidation and Reduction of Organic Compounds* (Englewood Cliffs, N.J.: Prentice-Hall, Inc., in preparation).

action; although it reduces aldehydes and ketones, it fails to reduce carboxyl groups. Lithium borohydride falls between these extremes; it reduces aldehydes and ketones very readily (at $0°$), reduces carboxylic esters with some reluctance (reflux temperature), and reduces acids only under very strenuous conditions.

Various unsaturated groups other than carbonyl functions often escape reduction by metal hydride reagents (see Table 3-1). This makes

Table 3-1

FUNCTIONAL GROUP SELECTIVITY WITH METAL
HYDRIDE REDUCING AGENTS†

Functional group	$NaBH_4$	$NaBH_4$ + LiCl	$NaBH_4$ + $AlCl_3$	$LiAlH_4$	$LiBH_4$
RCHO	+	+	+	+	+
R_2CO	+	+	+	+	+
RCOCl	+	+	+	+	+
RCO_2R'	−	+	+	+	+
RCO_2H	−	−	+	+	±
RCN	−	−	+	+	−
RNO_2	−	−	−	+	
$ArNO_2$	−			−	±
C=C	−	−	+	−	−
R—Halogen	±		+	+	−

† The selectivities indicated in this table are only approximate and may be influenced, among other things, by temperature.

possible many interesting and useful selective reductions, a few representative examples of which are shown in Fig. 3-32. The last two examples in Fig. 3-32 illustrate how hydride reductions can be used to convert carboxylic acids to aldehydes. Acid chlorides (see Fig. 3-17) or acylimidazoles (imidazolides) can be obtained from carboxylic acids and subsequently reduced to the aldehyde with the appropriate hydride reagent.

Hydride reductions may proceed in a stereoselective fashion and are governed by the forces described in Sec. 2.5. Bulky hydride reagents such as lithium aluminum hydride will tend to approach a carbonyl group from its less hindered face, and if this represents a significantly lower energy pathway, the reduction may give the product of kinetic control (also called "steric control"), as in the case of the conversion of bicyclo[2.2.1]-heptan-2-one to the corresponding alcohol shown in Fig. 3-33. However, if the carbonyl group is in a flexible system (e.g., 2-methylcyclohexanone) or if the two faces of the carbonyl group are comparably hindered, the major product of hydride reduction is usually the one of greater thermodynamic stability (which may also coincide with the product of kinetic control). With 2-methylcyclohexanone, for instance, the product of

$$CH_3CH{=}CHCHO + LiAlH_4 \text{ or } NaBH_4 \longrightarrow CH_3CH{=}CHCH_2OH$$

$$C_6H_5COCH_2CH_2CO_2H + LiBH_4 \longrightarrow C_6H_5CHOHCH_2CH_2CO_2H$$

$$\underset{\underset{NO_2}{|}}{(CH_3)_2CCH_2CH_2CO_2CH_3} + LiAlH_4 \xrightarrow{-40°} \underset{\underset{NO_2}{|}}{(CH_3)_2CCH_2CH_2CH_2OH}$$

$$Cl_2CHCOCl + LiAlH_4 \longrightarrow Cl_2CHCH_2OH$$

$$C_6H_5COCl + LiAlH[OC(CH_3)_3]_3† \longrightarrow C_6H_5CHO$$

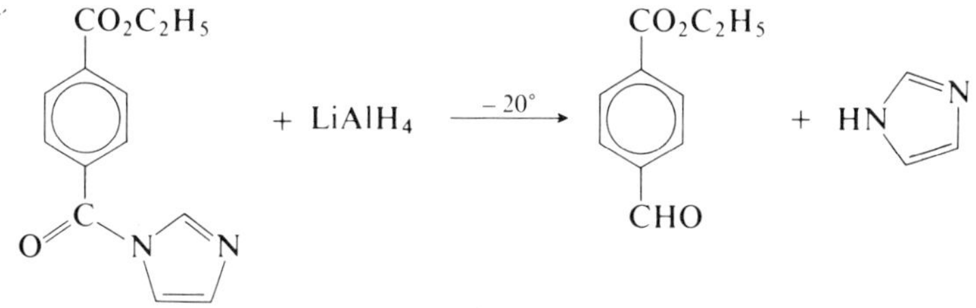

an acylimidazole
(imidazolide)

Fig. 3-32 Selective metal hydride reduction reactions.

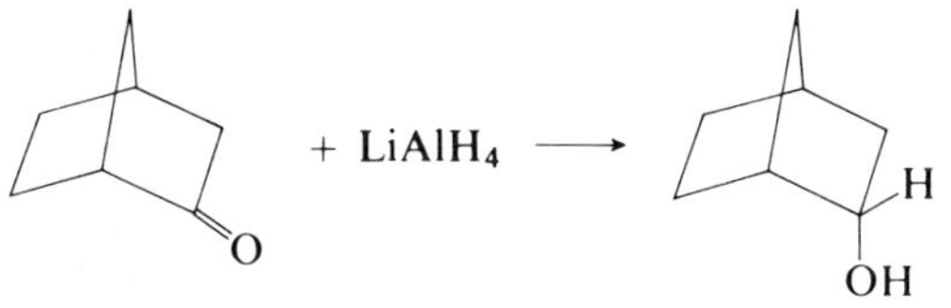

Fig. 3-33 Lithium aluminum hydride reduction of bicyclo [2.2.1]heptan-2-one.

lithium aluminum hydride reduction is mainly *trans*-2-methylcyclo-hexanol.

3.6 DIRECT ADDITION VERSUS CONJUGATE ADDITION VERSUS ADDITION-ELIMINATION

Although no categorical rules concerning addition versus addition-elimination reactions with hetero atom nucleophiles can be set forth, some approximate generalizations are possible:

Direct addition versus conjugate addition: With a given hetero atom nucleophile, conjugate addition is more likely to lead to stable product than is direct addition (see previous discussion).

Direct addition versus addition-elimination: With compounds contain-

† Prepared from three moles of *t*-C_4H_9OH and one mole of $LiAlH_4$.

ing both a class AA and a class AC carbonyl group, the reaction will be selective for one or the other of the carbonyls, depending upon the nature of the C group, as illustrated in Fig. 3-34. In general, acid chlorides and anhydrides are more likely to form a stable product with hetero atom nucleophiles than are simple aldehydes and ketones; esters and amides, on the other hand, are less likely to form a stable product with hetero atom nucleophiles than are simple aldehydes and ketones.

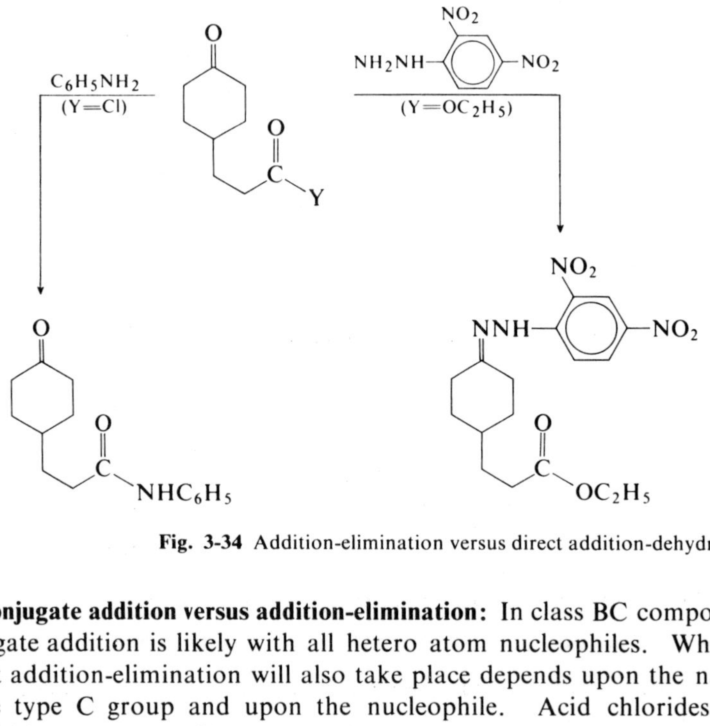

Fig. 3-34 Addition-elimination versus direct addition-dehydration.

Conjugate addition versus addition-elimination: In class BC compounds conjugate addition is likely with all hetero atom nucleophiles. Whether or not addition-elimination will also take place depends upon the nature of the type C group and upon the nucleophile. Acid chlorides and anhydrides are more likely to undergo both conjugate addition and addition-elimination; esters and amides are more likely to undergo only conjugate addition.

3.7 POLYFUNCTIONAL CARBONYL COMPOUNDS
(INTRAMOLECULAR REACTIONS)

The discussion to this point has been concerned almost entirely with examples of the various intermolecular reactions between carbonyl compounds and hetero atom nucleophiles. If the hetero atom nucleophilic center is located in a molecule which also contains a carbonyl group, an intramolecular interaction is possible; and if the separation between the carbonyl group and the hetero atom is such that a five-membered or six-membered ring will form, the driving force for the reaction is large. This is a consequence of a balance between the competing forces of proximity (which favor small rings) and strain factors (which favor larger rings). Reactions that proceed very incompletely in intermolecular systems may proceed very effectively in intramolecular systems. Perhaps the best known example of this phenomenon occurs in the sugars. Glucose, for instance, exists almost entirely in the cyclic hemiacetal form as the result of intramolecular interaction between the hydroxyl group on carbon-5 and the carbonyl group on carbon-1 (Fig. 3-35).[†]

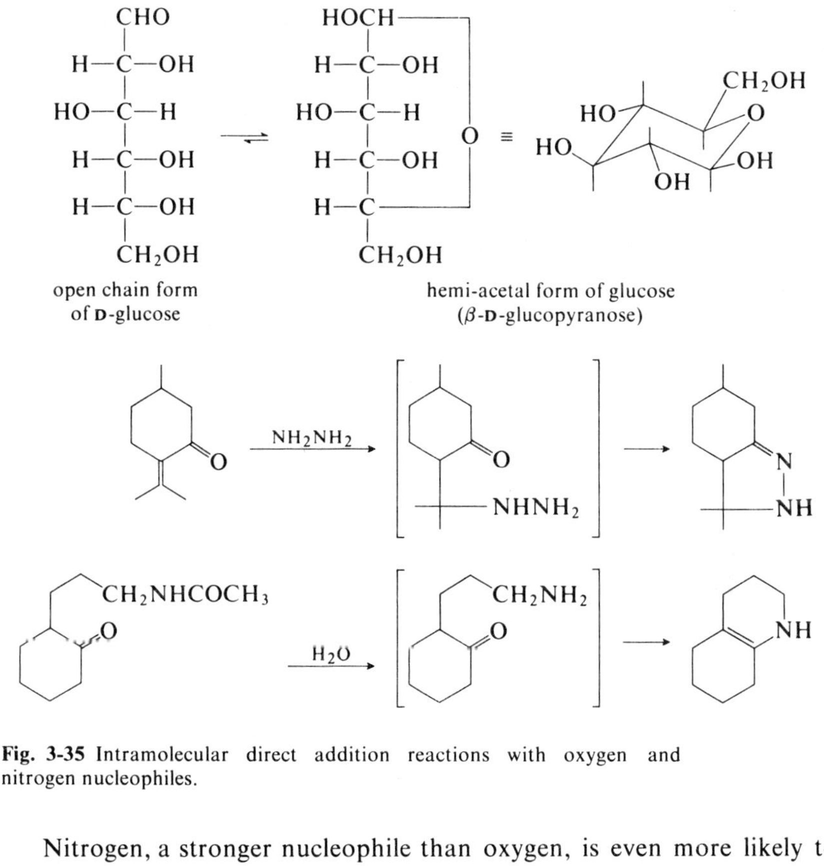

Fig. 3-35 Intramolecular direct addition reactions with oxygen and nitrogen nucleophiles.

Nitrogen, a stronger nucleophile than oxygen, is even more likely to engage in intramolecular reaction. The most familiar examples involve the reaction of α,β-unsaturated aldehydes and ketones with hydrazine, where the initial conjugate addition is followed by an intramolecular addition-dehydration to form pyrazoline derivatives (Fig. 3-35). Another illustration is provided by the product obtained from the hydrolysis of the

† R. L. Barker, *op. cit.*

keto amide shown in an earlier example (see Fig. 3-5), where the initially-formed keto amine immediately cyclizes via an addition-dehydration reaction (Fig. 3-35).

Intramolecular addition-elimination reactions occur readily in carboxylic acids and carboxylic acid derivatives which carry a group such as OH, SH, NH$_2$, etc. in the γ- or δ-position. The products of these reactions are cyclic carboxylic acid derivatives (lactones, lactams, etc.) and can easily be distinguished from those which form when the hetero atom substituent is in the α-position or in the β-position; α-substituted compounds lead to dimeric heterocyclic compounds (lactides from α-hydroxyl acids, diketopiperazines from α-amino acids), while β-substituted compounds lead to α,β-unsaturated carboxylic acids or carboxylic acid derivatives. Intramolecular addition-elimination reactions also occur readily in dicarboxylic acids in which the carboxyl groups are separated by two or three atoms. Examples of these processes are illustrated in Fig. 3-36.

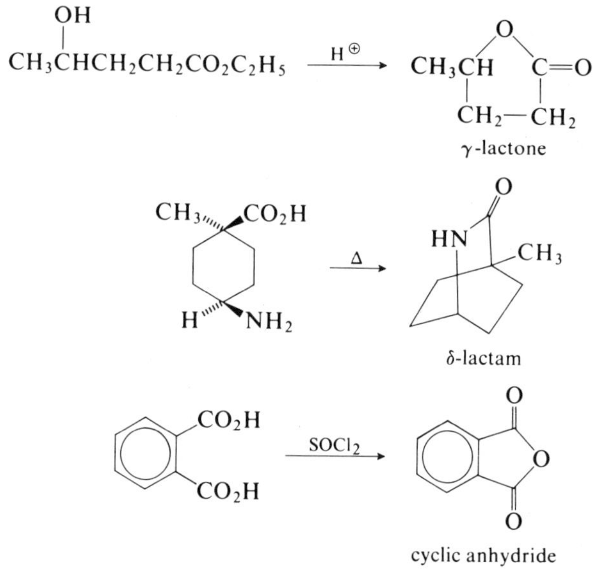

Fig. 3-36 Intramolecular addition-elimination reactions with oxygen and nitrogen nucleophiles.

PROBLEMS

1. Starting with chemicals available for less than $10 per 100 g, devise syntheses for the following compounds:

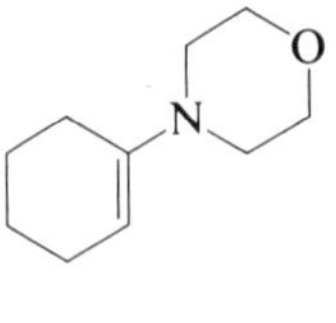

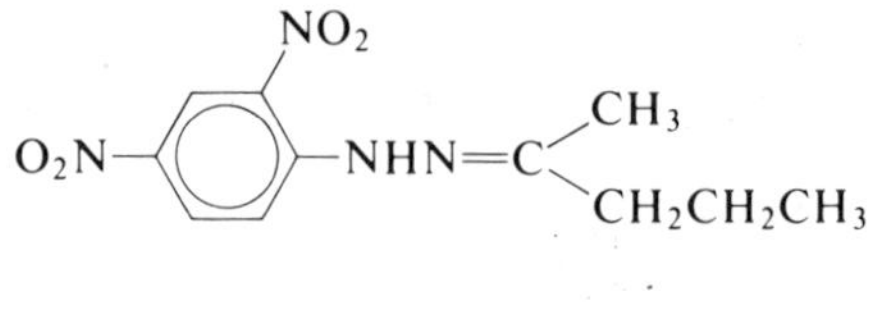

c. $CH_2CO_2(CH_2)_4CH_3$
   |
   CH_2CO_2H

d. $C_6H_5CH_2N(CH_2CH=CH_2)_2$

e. 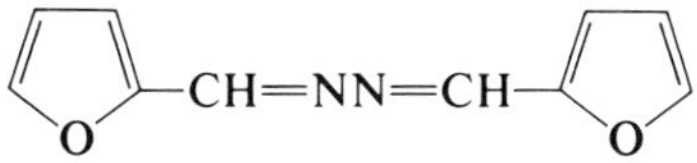 $-CH=NN=CH-$

2. Indicate what chemical methods could be used to effect the clean separation of the following mixtures of materials:

a. C_6H_5CHO and $C_6H_5COCH(CH_3)_2$

b. $(C_6H_5)_2CHCO_2H$ and 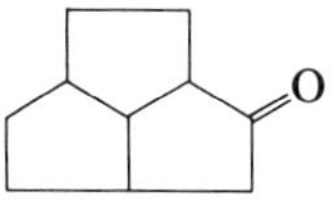 and

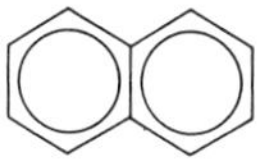

3. Indicate the reaction or reactions that might be employed to effect the following conversions:

a. 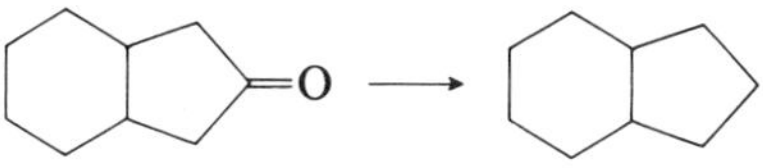 $\longrightarrow$

b. $C_6H_5COCH_2CH_3 \longrightarrow$

$$\begin{array}{c} C_6H_5 \diagdown \quad \diagup OC_2H_5 \\ C \\ CH_3CH_2 \diagup \quad \diagdown OC_2H_5 \end{array}$$

c. 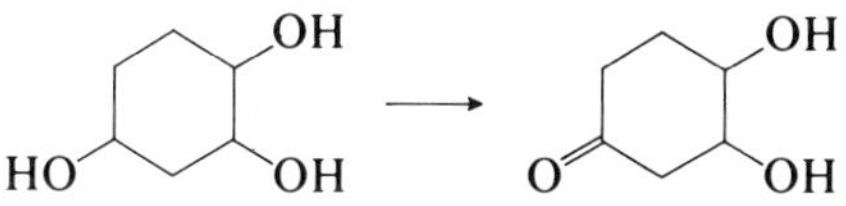 $\longrightarrow$

d. 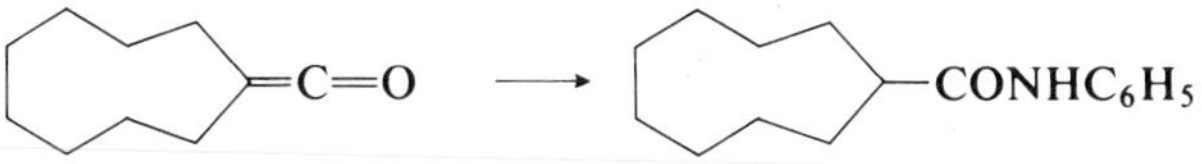 $=C=O \longrightarrow$ $-CONHC_6H_5$

e. 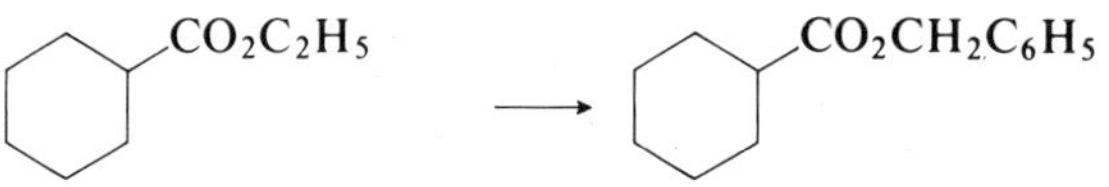 $CO_2C_2H_5 \longrightarrow$ $CO_2CH_2C_6H_5$

f. $CH_2=CHCOCH_3 \longrightarrow (CH_3)_2NCH_2CHCCH_3$

$$\begin{array}{c} OH \\ | \\ (CH_3)_2NCH_2CHCCH_3 \\ | \\ CN \end{array}$$

g. 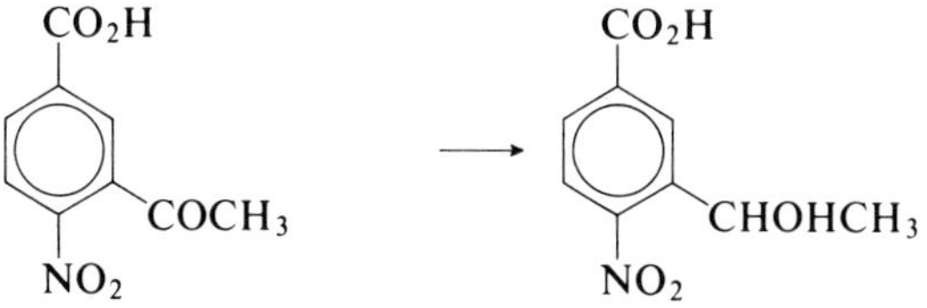 $\longrightarrow$

h.

i.

j. $CH_3CH{=}CHCOCH_3 \longrightarrow CH_3CH{=}CHCHCH_3$
$$\underset{\displaystyle OCOCH_3}{\big|}$$

4. Explain the following observations:

a. When optically active 2-hydroxy-4-methylcyclopentanone is treated with an excess of phenylhydrazine, the resulting product is optically inactive.

b. When an optically active sample of impure 2-methylcyclohexanone is purified via a Girard's reagent, the resulting product is optically inactive.

c. The conversion of 2-isopropylidene-5-methylcyclohexanone to the pyrazolone (see Fig. 3-35) gives one product, although two diastereoisomeric products are possible.

SELECTED REFERENCES

Many additional examples of the types of reactions discussed in this chapter are to be found in (a) R. C. Fuson, *Reactions of Organic Compounds: A Textbook for the Advanced Student,* New York: John Wiley & Sons, Inc., 1962; (b) E. E. Royals, *Advanced Organic Chemistry,* Englewood Cliffs, N.J.: Prentice-Hall, Inc., 1956. Detailed discussions of certain of the topics covered in this chapter are to be found in (a) H. A. Bruson, "Cyanoethylation," *Organic Reactions,* Vol. 5, p. 79 (1949); (b) E. D. Bergman, D. Ginsburg, and R. Pappo, "The Michael Reaction," *Organic Reactions,* Vol. 10, p. 179 (1959); (c) M. Hauser, "The Reactions of Mesityl Oxide," *Chem. Rev.,* **63**, 311 (1963); (d) J. E. Fernandez and T. W. G. Solomons, "Crotonaldehyde," *Chem. Rev.,* **62**, 485 (1962); (e) O. Wheeler, "Girard Reagents," *Chem. Rev.,* **62**, 205 (1962).

4

Nucleophilic Addition and Addition-Elimination Reactions with Carbon Nucleophiles

4.1 INTRODUCTION

The nucleophilic character of an element is related to its position in the periodic table and generally increases as this position shifts from the right of the table to the center; halide ions are very weak nucleophiles, oxygen centers are somewhat stronger, nitrogen centers are quite powerful, and carbon moieties carrying a full or fractional negative charge are very powerful nucleophiles. The addition and addition-elimination reactions between carbon nucleophiles and carbonyl compounds provide the subject matter for this chapter, the organization of which will be on the basis of the source of the carbon nucleophile.

4.2 STRONGLY POLARIZED (OR POLARIZABLE) COMPOUNDS AS SOURCES OF CARBON NUCLEOPHILES

Just as the electronegative element oxygen places a fractional positive charge on carbon when doubly bonded to it, so certain groups capable of releasing electrons can place a fractional negative charge on carbon when doubly bonded to it. Typical compounds in the latter class are the diazoalkanes, the phosphorus ylids, and the sulfur ylids pictured in Fig. 4-1. To the extent that the structures in the lower line of Fig. 4-1 contribute to the resonance hybrids, these compounds are nucleophiles at the carbon atom and may react as such. They undergo direct addition with class AA compounds to give intermediates which can collapse in three ways, as illustrated in Fig. 4-2. Pathways a and b are examples of type Z addition-elimination, as discussed in Sec. 2.4 (see Fig. 2-18), and proceed because the nucleophiles carry good "leaving groups" (i.e., N_2 and $(CH_3)_2S$ in the case of diazoalkanes and sulfur ylids, respectively). With diazoalkanes,

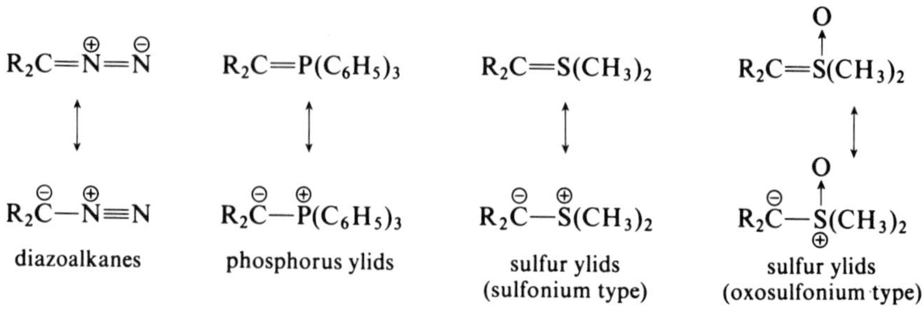

$$R_2C=\overset{\oplus}{N}=\overset{\ominus}{N} \qquad R_2C=P(C_6H_5)_3 \qquad R_2C=S(CH_3)_2 \qquad R_2C=\overset{O}{\underset{\uparrow}{S}}(CH_3)_2$$

$$\updownarrow \qquad\qquad \updownarrow \qquad\qquad \updownarrow \qquad\qquad \updownarrow$$

$$\overset{\ominus}{R_2C}-\overset{\oplus}{N}\equiv N \qquad \overset{\ominus}{R_2C}-\overset{\oplus}{P}(C_6H_5)_3 \qquad \overset{\ominus}{R_2C}-\overset{\oplus}{S}(CH_3)_2 \qquad \overset{\ominus}{R_2C}-\overset{O}{\underset{\overset{\uparrow}{\oplus}}{S}}(CH_3)_2$$

diazoalkanes　　　　phosphorus ylids　　　　sulfur ylids　　　　　sulfur ylids
　　　　　　　　　　　　　　　　　　　　　(sulfonium type)　　　(oxosulfonium type)

Fig. 4-1 Strongly polarized (or polarizable) compounds which act as carbon nucleophiles (type $R_2C=Z$ carbon nucleophiles).

both pathways *a* and *b* are frequently followed, although path *b* usually predominates; with the sulfur ylids, path *a* is preferred. Phosphorus ylids, on the other hand, usually follow path *c*, which represents a type of "reorganization reaction" (i.e., oxygen and carbon trade places). Reactions involving these several species furnish useful preparations for homologous aldehydes and ketones, oxides, and olefins, as illustrated in Fig. 4-3.

The phosphorus ylid reaction, often referred to as the "Wittig reaction," is particularly versatile in its applicability to the synthesis of a wide variety of mono-substituted, di-substituted, and tri-substituted olefins. The "Wittig reagent" is prepared by allowing the appropriate alkyl halide to interact with triphenylphosphine, followed by treatment of the resulting phosphonium salt with a strong base, as illustrated in Fig. 4-4.

Conjugate reactions can also be demonstrated with these reagents, and two pathways are observed, as illustrated in Fig. 4-5. Path *a* of Fig. 4-5 is characteristic of diazoalkanes and corresponds to an addition reaction; path *b* of Fig. 4-5 is characteristic of sulfur ylids and phosphorus ylids and corresponds to a type Z conjugate addition-elimination reaction.

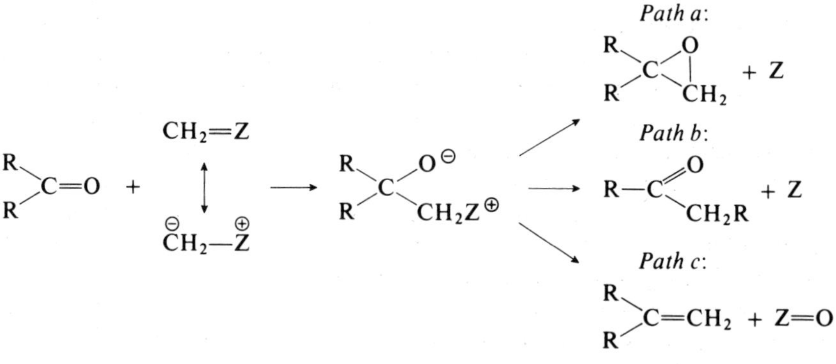

Fig. 4-2 Reactions of $R_2C=Z$ type carbon nucleophiles with class AA carbonyl compounds.

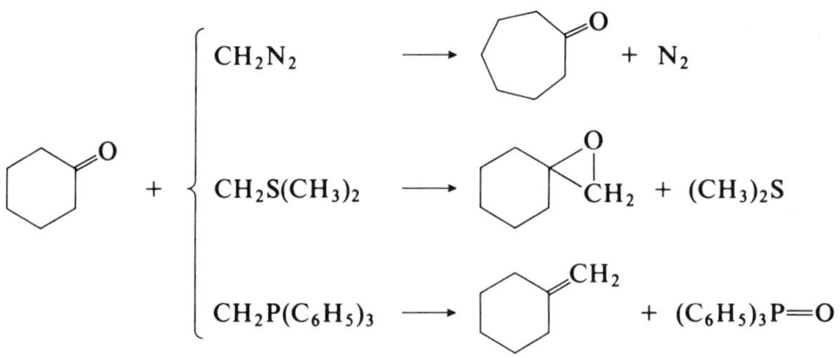

Fig. 4-3 Reactions of $R_2C=Z$ type nucleophiles with cyclohexanone.

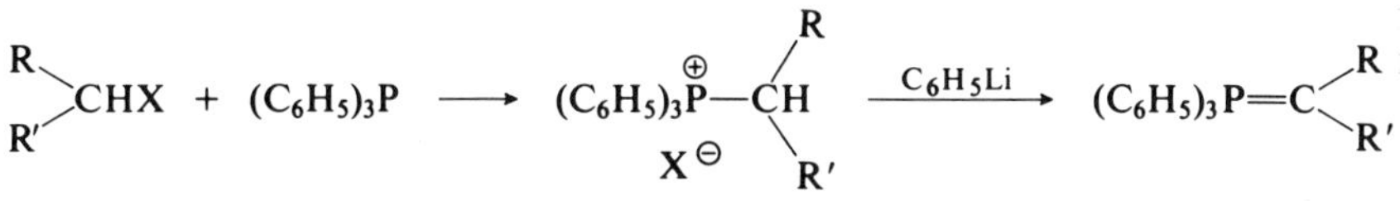

Fig. 4-4 Preparation of phosphorus ylids ("Wittig reagents").

In the case of the sulfur ylids it is interesting to note that dimethyl-sulfonium methylide reacts almost exclusively by direct type Z addition-elimination with class AB compounds, whereas dimethyloxosulfonium methylide reacts almost exclusively by conjugate type Z addition-elimination, as illustrated by the examples in Fig. 4-6.

Type $R_2C=Z$ carbon nucleophiles may undergo direct addition-elimination with acid chlorides, as illustrated in Fig. 4-7. Diazoketones are particularly useful synthesis intermediates, for they take part in a variety of reactions of the type shown in Fig. 4-8. Of special interest is the last reaction of this group, for it represents the terminal step in a sequence known as the Arndt-Eistert synthesis. This is a method for preparing the next higher homolog of a carboxylic acid by the following

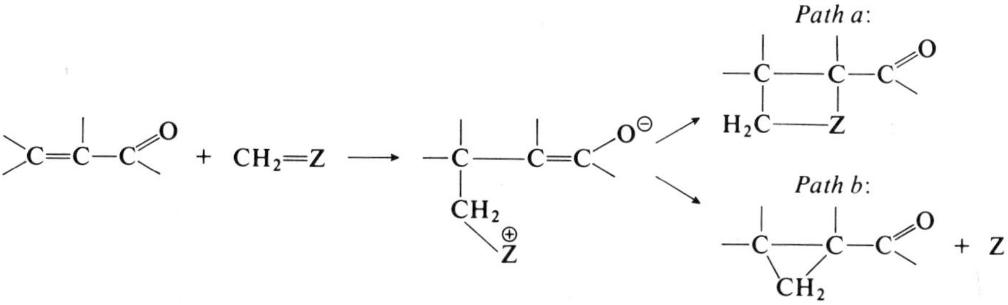

Fig. 4-5 Reactions of $R_2C=Z$ type carbon nucleophiles with class AB, BB, and BC carbonyl compounds.

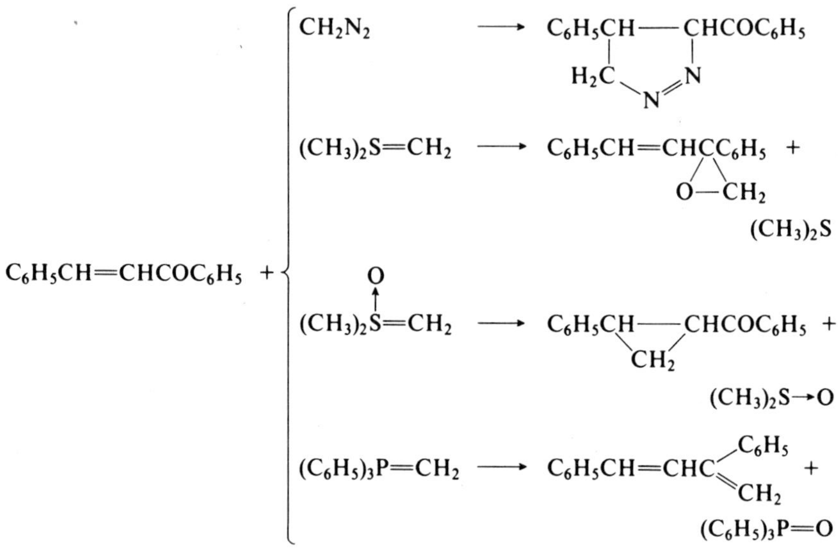

$$C_6H_5CH=CHCOC_6H_5 \ + \begin{cases} CH_2N_2 \longrightarrow C_6H_5CH\!\!-\!\!CHCOC_6H_5 \\ \qquad\qquad\quad \overset{H_2C}{\underset{N\diagdown N}{\diagup}}N \\[2mm] (CH_3)_2S=CH_2 \longrightarrow C_6H_5CH=CHCC_6H_5 \ + \\ \qquad\qquad\qquad\qquad \overset{}{\underset{O-CH_2}{}} \\ \qquad\qquad\qquad\qquad\qquad (CH_3)_2S \\[2mm] \qquad\qquad O \\ \qquad\qquad\uparrow \\ (CH_3)_2S=CH_2 \longrightarrow C_6H_5CH\!\!-\!\!CHCOC_6H_5 \ + \\ \qquad\qquad\qquad\qquad \overset{}{\underset{CH_2}{}} \\ \qquad\qquad\qquad\qquad\qquad (CH_3)_2S\!\rightarrow\!O \\[2mm] (C_6H_5)_3P=CH_2 \longrightarrow C_6H_5CH=CHC\overset{C_6H_5}{\underset{CH_2}{\diagup\!\!\!\diagdown}} \ + \\ \qquad\qquad\qquad\qquad\qquad (C_6H_5)_3P=O \end{cases}$$

Fig. 4-6 Reactions of $R_2C=Z$ type carbon nucleophiles with benzalaceto-phenone.

series of reactions: $RCO_2H \rightarrow RCOCl \rightarrow RCOCHN_2 \rightarrow RCH_2CO_2CH_3 \rightarrow RCH_2CO_2H$.

4.3 ORGANOMETALLIC COMPOUNDS AS SOURCES OF CARBON NUCLEOPHILES

The replacement of hydrogen by a metal atom in R—H produces a species known as an organometallic compound. If the hydrogen in R—H

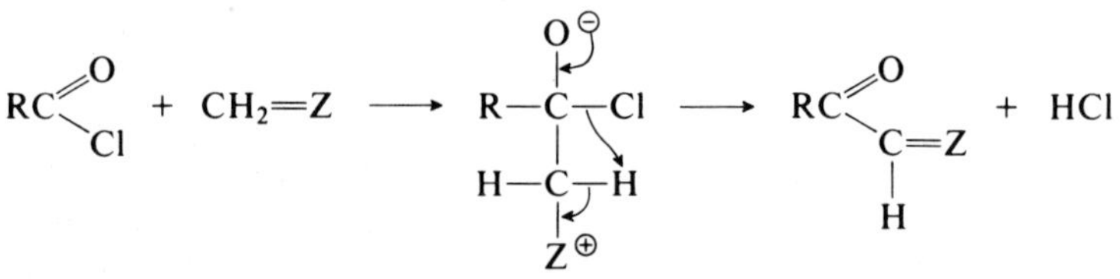

$$RC\!\!\overset{O}{\underset{Cl}{\diagup\!\!\!\diagdown}} + CH_2=Z \longrightarrow R\!-\!\overset{O^{\ominus}}{\underset{\underset{Z^{\oplus}}{\overset{|}{C}-H}}{\overset{|}{\underset{|}{C}}-Cl}} \longrightarrow RC\!\!\overset{O}{\underset{\overset{|}{\underset{H}{C=Z}}}{\diagup\!\!\!\diagdown}} + HCl$$

Diazoketone Synthesis:

$$RCOCl + CH_2N_2 \longrightarrow RCOCHN_2$$

Acyl Ylid Synthesis:

$$RCOCl + (C_6H_5)_3P=CH_2 \longrightarrow RCOCHP(C_6H_5)_3$$

Fig. 4-7 Reactions of $R_2C=Z$ type carbon nucleophiles with class AC car-bonyl compounds.

Synthesis of α-Halo Ketones:

$$RCOCHN_2 + HX \longrightarrow RCOCH_2X$$

Synthesis of α,α-Dihalo Ketones:

$$RCOCHN_2 + X_2 \longrightarrow RCOCHX_2$$

Wolff Rearrangement:

$$RCOCHN_2 + CH_3OH \xrightarrow{\ C_6H_5CO_2Ag\ } RCH_2CO_2CH_3$$

Fig. 4-8 Syntheses with diazoketones.

is sufficiently acidic, the replacement can be effected directly by the action of a metal or a strong base. For instance, hydrogen cyanide produces $CN^{\ominus}$ with alkali metals or moderately strong bases such as hydroxide ion, and acetylenes produce $RC{\equiv}C^{\ominus}$ with certain metals or strong bases such as sodium amide. If R—H is more weakly acidic, however, indirect means may be necessary as, for instance, conversion to the corresponding halide, RX, followed by treatment with a metal (e.g., $RX + Mg \rightarrow RMgX$). The R-metal bond in the organometallic compound so obtained is polarized in the direction which concentrates electrons on R and removes electrons from the metal, e.g., $R^{\delta\ominus} \cdots metal^{\delta\oplus}$. The extent of polarization depends very strongly on the ability of the R portion to accommodate a negative charge which, in turn, is directly related to the acidity of R—H. Thus, the polarity of the carbon-metal bond diminishes from $N{\equiv}C \cdots Li$ to $RC{\equiv}C \cdots Li$ to $H_3C \cdots Li$ as the acidity of the corresponding acids diminishes from HCN (pK_A 9.15), to $RC{\equiv}CH$ (pK_A about 20), to CH_4 (pK_A about 40).

The nucleophilic character of a carbon nucleophile is inversely related to the stability of $R^{\ominus}$ and the acidity of R—H. One of the weakest carbon nucleophiles, then, is hydrogen cyanide. As has already been discussed in Chap. 2, however, it is sufficiently powerful to give moderately stable direct addition products with many class AA compounds and to give very stable conjugate addition products with class AB, BB, and BC compounds. Cyanohydrins are useful reagents for preparing a variety of compounds, as illustrated in Fig. 4-9. Cyanide ion is intermediate between bisulfite ion and hydroxide ion in nucleophilic power, as indicated by the fact that cyanohydrins can be formed from a bisulfite addition product and sodium cyanide, but are decomposed by aqueous sodium hydroxide. This is what would be predicted from a knowledge of the relative acidities of the conjugate acids of the nucleophilic species involved (i.e., pK_A of H_2SO_3 is 1.77, pK_A of HCN is 9.15, pK_A of H_2O is 15.7).

A somewhat more powerful nucleophilic reagent than cyanide ion is the acetylenide anion, which adds very effectively to class AA compounds to give useful synthesis intermediates, as shown in Fig. 4-10. Whereas

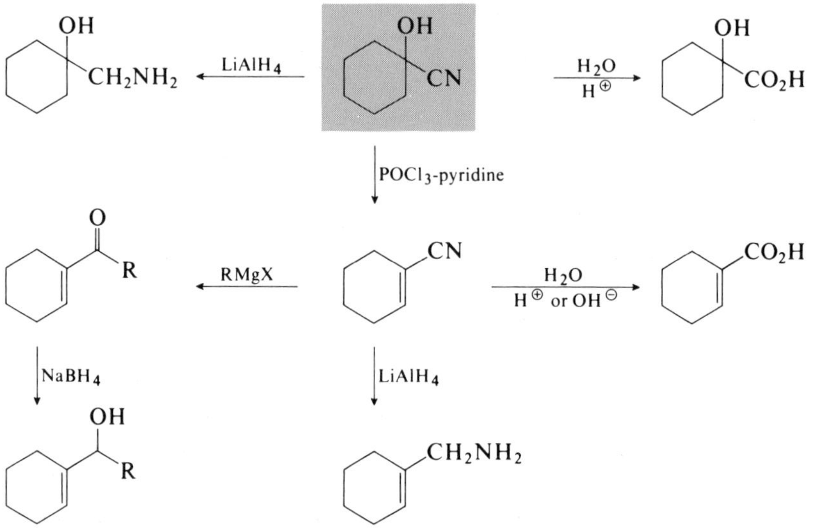

Fig. 4-9 Cyanohydrins as useful synthesis intermediates.

cyanide ion is a weaker nucleophilic agent than hydroxide or alkoxide ion, the acetylenide anion is a stronger nucleophile, as illustrated by the reaction shown in Fig. 4-11 in which the carbonyl addition reaction takes place at the acetylenic carbon rather than at the oxygen.

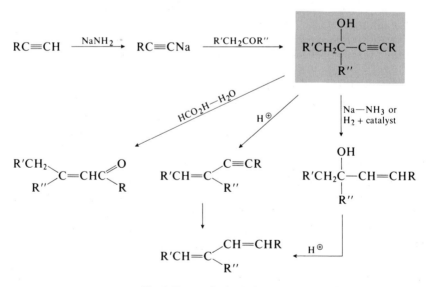

Fig. 4-10 Acetylenic alcohols as useful synthesis intermediates.

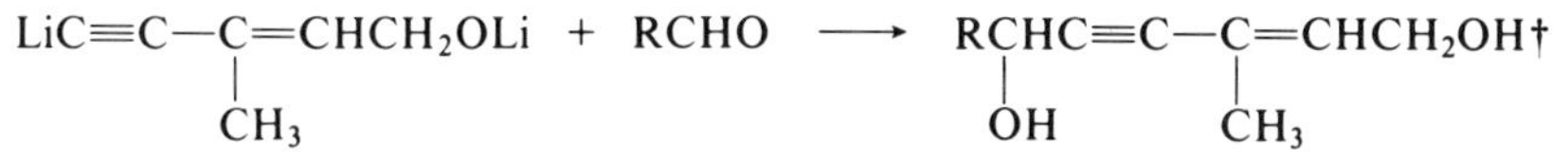

$$LiC \equiv C - \underset{\underset{CH_3}{|}}{C} = CHCH_2OLi \ + \ RCHO \ \longrightarrow \ R\underset{\underset{OH}{|}}{C}HC \equiv C - \underset{\underset{CH_3}{|}}{C} = CHCH_2OH\dagger$$

Fig. 4-11 Reaction of a di-functional nucleophile.

Many compounds of the general structure

$$-\overset{|}{\underset{|}{C}} \cdots \text{metal} \quad \text{and} \quad \overset{}{\underset{}{>}}C = \overset{|}{C} \cdots \text{metal}$$

are considerably more nucleophilic than cyanide and acetylenide anions and may be capable of adding in an essentially irreversible fashion to carbonyl compounds. The nucleophilic character, however, is quite dependent on the particular metal, the more ionic the bond the more nucleophilic the R portion. For instance, C—Li bonds have about 43% ionic character, C—Mg bonds about 34%, C—Al bonds about 22%, C—Cd bonds about 15%, and C—Hg bonds about 9%. Thus, organo-lithium and organomagnesium compounds are powerful nucleophilic agents and add to almost all carbonyl groups; organocadmium compounds are quite selective in carbonyl addition reactions; and organo-mercury compounds are rather inert. Organolithium and organomag-nesium compounds (Grignard reagents) furnish unusually versatile reagents for converting aldehydes to secondary alcohols or ketones to tertiary alcohols, as illustrated by the representative examples in Fig. 4-12.

Class D carbonyl compounds react with organolithium and Grignard reagents via addition, as illustrated by the examples in Fig. 4-13. Par-ticular attention is directed to the reaction with carbon dioxide, which provides a synthesis for carboxylic acids.

The reactions that have been discussed thus far have focused on the attack of the nucleophilic reagent at the electrophilic center of the car-bonyl carbon, and little attention has been given to the role of the oxygen atom of the carbonyl group or to the role of the cationic species which must at some point add to the carbonyl oxygen. In the case of Grignard reagents, these latter details must be considered; it is thought that the initial interaction between a carbonyl compound and a Grignard reagent involves the formation of a coordination complex in which the carbonyl oxygen acts as the Lewis base (see Sec. 1.12) and the magnesium acts as the Lewis acid, as illustrated in Fig. 4-14. The formation of this coordina-tion complex, requiring the displacement of an ether molecule from the $RMgX(OEt)_2$ complex, may be the slow step (rate-determining step)

† The initially formed product is actually the dilithium salt from which the diol is formed only upon treatment with a proton donor, e.g., water or aqueous acid. In many of the succeeding illustrations of this general type of reaction, the hydrolysis step is implicit, and the product will be shown in the protonated form.

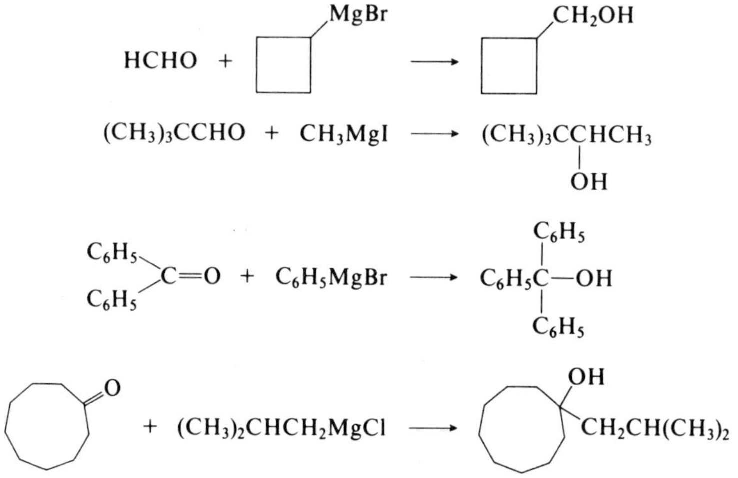

HCHO + [ ]–MgBr ⟶ [ ]–CH$_2$OH

(CH$_3$)$_3$CCHO + CH$_3$MgI ⟶ (CH$_3$)$_3$CCHCH$_3$
$\qquad\qquad\qquad\qquad\qquad\qquad$ |
$\qquad\qquad\qquad\qquad\qquad\qquad$ OH

$$\begin{array}{c} C_6H_5 \\ \diagdown \\ \diagup \\ C_6H_5 \end{array} C{=}O \; + \; C_6H_5MgBr \; \longrightarrow \; \begin{array}{c} C_6H_5 \\ | \\ C_6H_5C{-}OH \\ | \\ C_6H_5 \end{array}$$

⬡=O + (CH$_3$)$_2$CHCH$_2$MgCl ⟶ ⬡⟨OH⟩CH$_2$CH(CH$_3$)$_2$

Fig. 4-12 Preparation of secondary and tertiary alcohols via Grignard reagents.

which is then succeeded by faster reactions. For the formation of "normal product," the succeeding reaction may involve a second molecule of the Grignard reagent leading to a new complex (pseudo six-membered ring intermediate) which might break down in the manner depicted in Fig. 4-15. Surprisingly, however, the accurate description of this important reaction remains obscure, and this mechanism must be accorded even more skepticism than most of the others presented in this book.

Grignard reagents frequently react with carbonyl compounds by routes other than direct addition and lead to "abnormal products." The two most important of these reactions are "enolization" and "reduction" and can be explained in terms of the alternative modes of decomposition of the initially-formed complex shown in Fig. 4-15. The enolization reaction is extensive when formidable steric interaction between ketone and Grignard reagent is encountered as, for instance, in the reaction of di-

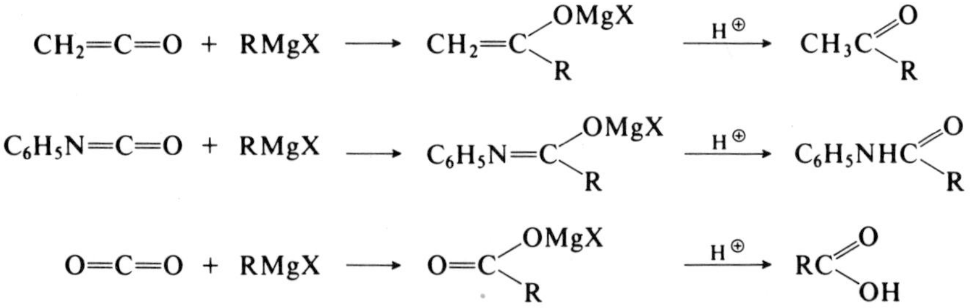

$$CH_2{=}C{=}O + RMgX \longrightarrow CH_2{=}C\begin{array}{c} \diagup OMgX \\ \diagdown R \end{array} \xrightarrow{H^\oplus} CH_3C\begin{array}{c} \diagup O \\ \diagdown R \end{array}$$

$$C_6H_5N{=}C{=}O + RMgX \longrightarrow C_6H_5N{=}C\begin{array}{c} \diagup OMgX \\ \diagdown R \end{array} \xrightarrow{H^\oplus} C_6H_5NHC\begin{array}{c} \diagup O \\ \diagdown R \end{array}$$

$$O{=}C{=}O + RMgX \longrightarrow O{=}C\begin{array}{c} \diagup OMgX \\ \diagdown R \end{array} \xrightarrow{H^\oplus} RC\begin{array}{c} \diagup O \\ \diagdown OH \end{array}$$

Fig. 4-13 Reactions of class D compounds with Grignard reagents.

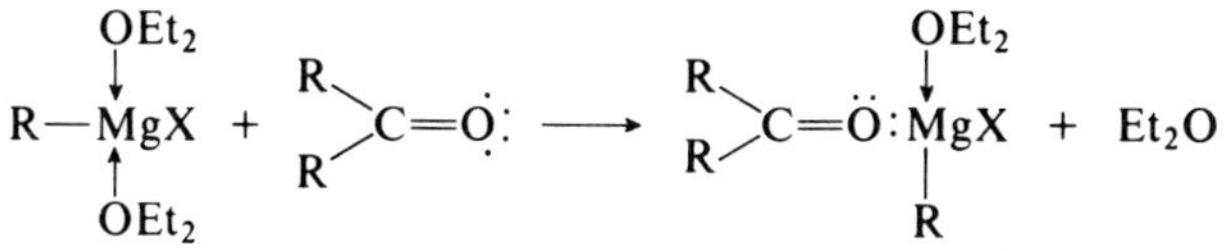

Fig. 4-14 Complex formation between Grignard reagents and carbonyl compounds.

isopropyl ketone with isopropylmagnesium bromide. The reduction reaction may likewise become significant when steric interactions are severe and when the Grignard reagent possesses a β-hydrogen which, it is postulated, can be transferred to the carbonyl group via a cyclic process, as shown in Fig. 4-15.

Although organomagnesium and organolithium compounds usually behave in a comparable fashion, striking differences can occasionally be demonstrated, as in the reaction of the isopropyl organometallic with diisopropyl ketone. Whereas isopropylmagnesium bromide gives 65% of the reduction product and 29% of the enolization product (no normal addition product), isopropyllithium yields the normal product. Even more striking is the addition of t-butyllithium to di-t-butyl ketone to give tri-t-butyl carbinol in high yield. This difference is perhaps due to the

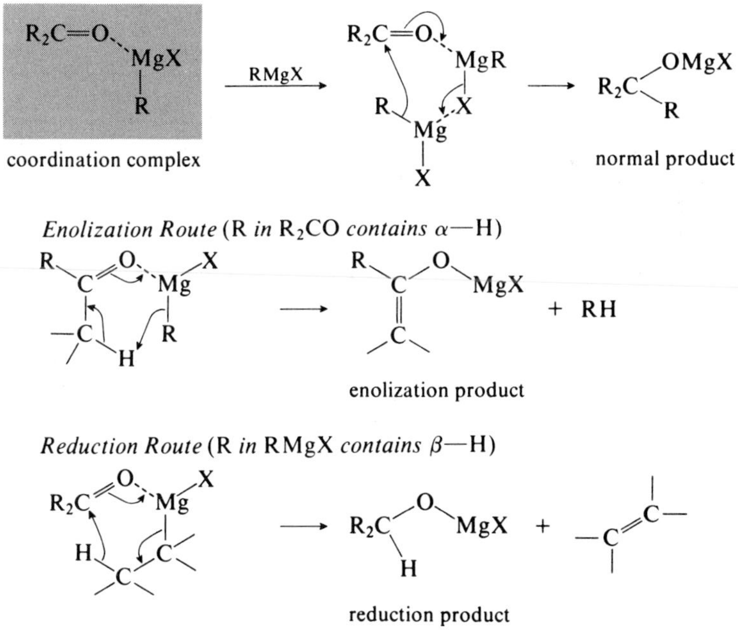

coordination complex   normal product

Enolization Route (R in R_2CO *contains* α—H)

enolization product

Reduction Route (R in $RMgX$ *contains* β—H)

reduction product

Fig. 4-15 Pathways of decomposition of coordination complex of Grignard reagent and carbonyl compound.

ability of the organolithium compound to form a coordination complex which can directly break down to addition product without the intervention of a second molecule of organometallic reagent, as schematically illustrated in Fig. 4-16.

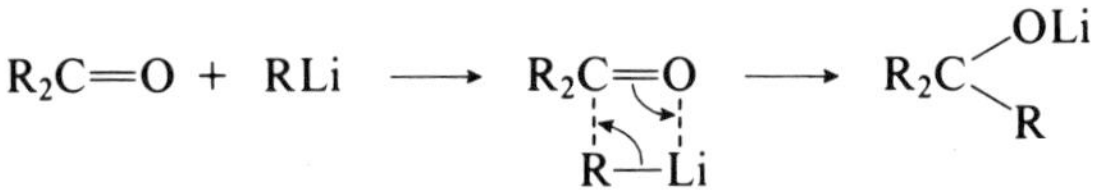

$$R_2C{=}O + RLi \longrightarrow R_2C{=}O \longrightarrow R_2C{\overset{OLi}{\underset{R}{\diagdown}}}$$

Fig. 4-16 Complex formation between organolithium compounds and carbonyl compounds.

The conjugate addition of Grignard reagents was discussed in Sec. 2.3, where it was pointed out that steric factors are important in determining the amount of direct addition versus conjugate addition. Since both of these reactions are essentially irreversible with Grignard reagents (as contrasted with certain other nucleophiles such as cyanide and bisulfite), the amount of product resulting from these two pathways is important in determining the synthetic usefulness of the process. Frequently, both types of products are formed in comparable amounts which not only reduces the yield of desired material but also poses a problem in purification (see Table 2-3). Some control may be exerted, however, by the choice of organometallic reagent: (a) aliphatic Grignard reagents are more prone to conjugate addition than are aromatic Grignard reagents; (b) organolithium reagents are more prone to direct addition than are the corresponding Grignard reagents. Another device that sometimes promotes conjugate addition is the inclusion of a copper compound (e.g., Cu_2Cl_2, $CuBr_2$, $Cu(OAc)_2$, etc.) in the reaction mixture. In addition to 1,4-conjugate addition, 1,6- and 1,8-conjugate additions are also known, as illustrated in Fig. 4-17.

Before discussing addition-elimination reactions, the great utility of organometallics in direct addition and conjugate addition reactions must again be emphasized by noting several additional examples shown in Fig. 4-18.

With appropriate carbonyl compounds the addition-elimination pathway is also available to organometallic reagents. The weakly nucleophilic cyanide ion will engage in addition-elimination only with acid halides (to form acyl cyanides, RCOCN), but the strongly nucleophilic organolithium and organomagnesium compounds will react with all carboxylic acids and carboxylic acid derivatives. If the carboxylic acid derivative contains a hydrogen attached to a hetero atom ("active hydrogen"), the first reaction will be at this site. Thus, carboxylic acids themselves and unalkylated and monoalkylated amides react as shown in Fig. 4-19. However, if there is no active hydrogen in the carboxylic acid derivative, an

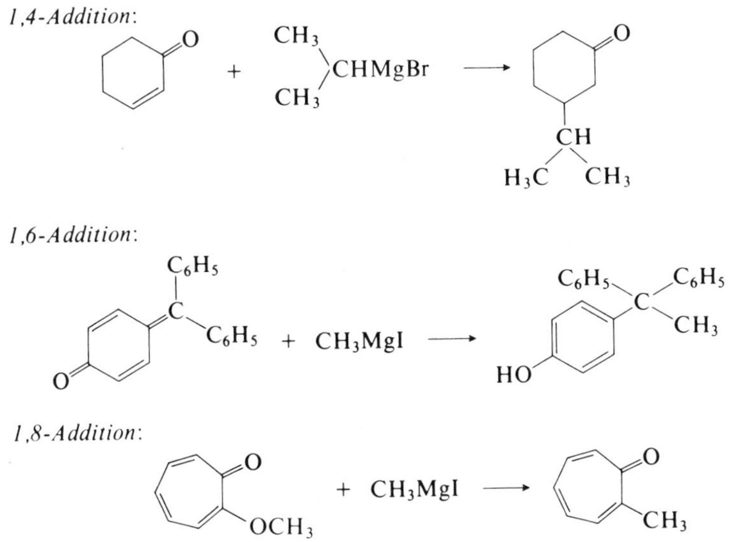

1,4-Addition:

1,6-Addition:

1,8-Addition:

Fig. 4-17 Conjugate addition reactions of Grignard reagents.

addition-elimination reaction will take place to give a ketone which, ordinarily, will react with additional organometallic reagent to furnish an alcohol. The several types of alcohols that are available by this procedure are shown in Fig. 4-20. Under certain conditions the reaction can be interrupted after only one mole of RMgX has reacted and can be used as a preparative method for ketones. One technique appropriate for this is called the "inverse procedure" and involves the addition of the Grignard reagent to the acid halide (instead of the addition of the acid halide

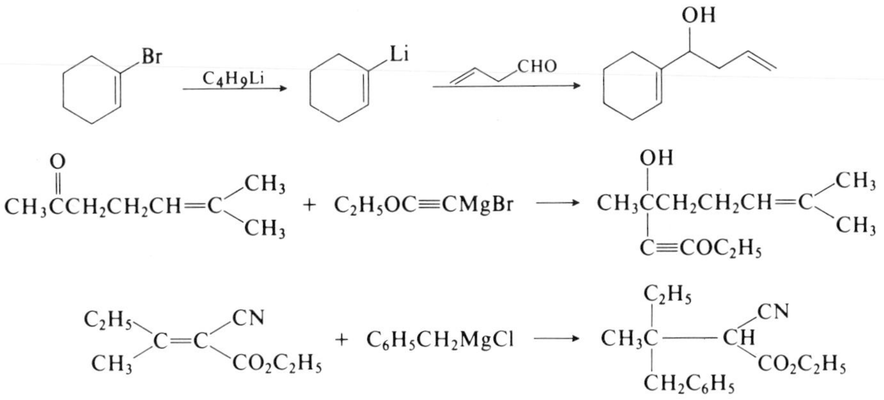

Fig. 4-18 Direct addition and conjugate addition reactions of organometallic reagents.

$$RCO_2H + RMgX \longrightarrow RCO_2MgX + RH$$

$$RCONH_2 + RLi \longrightarrow RCONHLi + RH$$

$$RCONHR + RMgX \longrightarrow \underset{\underset{MgX}{|}}{RCONR} + RH$$

Fig. 4-19 Reaction of organometallic reagents with compounds containing "active hydrogen."†

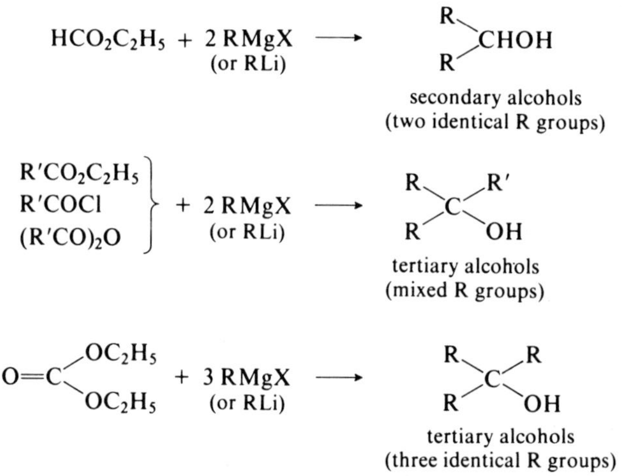

to the Grignard reagent, which is the ordinary procedure). The purpose of the inverse order of addition is to maintain, throughout the course of the reaction, an excess of the acid halide, which being more reactive than the ketone,‡ reacts preferentially with the limited amount of Grignard reagent present at any moment.

A sometimes more convenient alternative is to employ an organocadmium reagent, as illustrated in Fig. 4-21, which works because these reagents are very much more reactive toward acid chlorides than toward ketones. Still another procedure involves the addition of an organolithium reagent to the lithium salt of a carboxylic acid. In practice the reaction is carried out by simply using two moles of organolithium reagent per mole of carboxylic acid. The first mole reacts with the active hydrogen to form the salt, and the second mole adds to the carbonyl group to give a dilithium salt which is stable until treated with acid, thereupon hydrolyzing to

$$HCO_2C_2H_5 + 2\,RMgX \longrightarrow \underset{R}{\overset{R}{>}}CHOH$$
$$\text{(or RLi)}$$

secondary alcohols
(two identical R groups)

$$\left.\begin{array}{l} R'CO_2C_2H_5 \\ R'COCl \\ (R'CO)_2O \end{array}\right\} + 2\,RMgX \longrightarrow \underset{R}{\overset{R}{>}}\underset{OH}{\overset{R'}{<}}C$$
$$\text{(or RLi)}$$

tertiary alcohols
(mixed R groups)

$$O{=}C\underset{OC_2H_5}{\overset{OC_2H_5}{<}} + 3\,RMgX \longrightarrow \underset{R}{\overset{R}{>}}\underset{OH}{\overset{R}{<}}C$$
$$\text{(or RLi)}$$

tertiary alcohols
(three identical R groups)

Fig. 4-20 Synthesis of secondary and tertiary alcohols via Grignard reagents or organolithium reagents.

† If the salts that form in the manner shown here are sufficiently soluble in the reaction medium (usually diethyl ether), a carbonyl addition or addition-elimination reaction may take place to produce ketones or alcohols.

‡ The greater reactivity of RCOCl as compared with RCOCH₃ may be partly steric in origin but must also be ascribed to the electron-withdrawing effect of the halogen which is only partially offset by its resonance-electromeric electron-releasing effect (see Sec. 1.8).

ketone, as illustrated in Fig. 4-22. A comparable reaction with Grignard reagents is less likely to take place, because the initially formed halomagnesium carboxylate salt is much less soluble than the lithium salt and precipitates from solution.

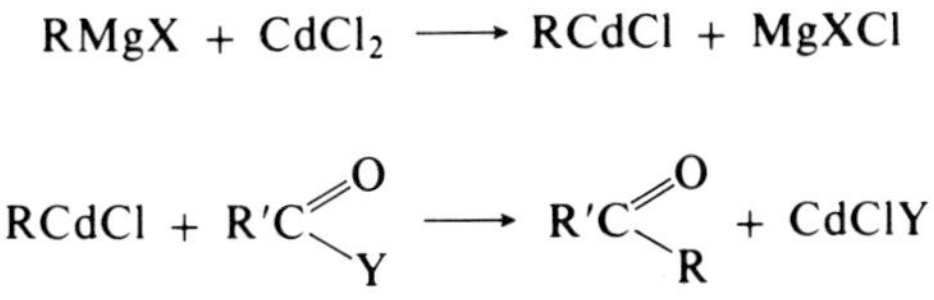

$$RMgX + CdCl_2 \longrightarrow RCdCl + MgXCl$$

$$RCdCl + R'C\overset{O}{\underset{Y}{\diagup}} \longrightarrow R'C\overset{O}{\underset{R}{\diagup}} + CdClY$$

Fig. 4-21 Preparation of ketones via organocadmium reagents.

4.4 ACTIVE METHYLENE COMPOUNDS AS SOURCES OF CARBON NUCLEOPHILES

The proton-donating capacity of carbonyl compounds having one or more α-hydrogens has been discussed in Sec. 1.12. Such compounds are examples of the more general situation in which structures H—C—Y are

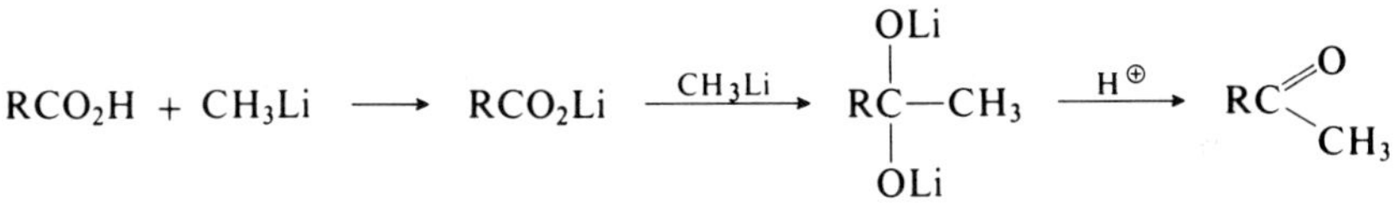

$$RCO_2H + CH_3Li \longrightarrow RCO_2Li \xrightarrow{CH_3Li} \underset{\underset{OLi}{|}}{\overset{\overset{OLi}{|}}{RC}}-CH_3 \xrightarrow{H^\oplus} RC\overset{O}{\underset{CH_3}{\diagup}}$$

Fig. 4-22 Preparation of ketones from carboxylic acids and organolithium reagents.

acidic if the Y group has the ability to delocalize a negative charge away from carbon. In addition to carbonyl groups serving this purpose, other groups such as NO_2, CN, SO_2R, C=C, Aryl, C=N, and pyridyl also suffice. Compounds of the type listed in Table 4-1 are acidic enough to yield anions, when treated with sufficiently strong bases, and are often referred to as "active methylene compounds." The carbanions from active methylene compounds are intermediate in nucleophilic character between Grignard-type organometallic reagents and cyanide ion (as judged by the acidities shown in Table 4-1) and have the capacity to react with carbonyl compounds.

Unlike most of the other nucleophiles that have been considered so far, the anions from active methylene compounds are "ambident anions," i.e., the electron density

Table 4-1

ACIDITIES OF $-\overset{|}{\underset{|}{C}}-H$ IN ACTIVE

METHYLENE COMPOUNDS

Compound	pK_A
$CH_3\overset{\downarrow}{\underset{O}{S}}CH_3$	40
$(C_6H_5)_3CH$	40
$CH_3CON(CH_3)_2$	30
$CH_3CO_2C_2H_5$	24
CH_3COCH_3	19
$CH_2(CO_2C_2H_5)_2$	13
$CH_2(CN)_2$	11
$CH_3COCH_2CO_2C_2H_5$	11
$CH_2(CN)CO_2C_2H_5$	9
$CH_2(COCH_3)_2$	9

is concentrated at more than one point as a result of electron delocalization. For instance, the anion from acetaldehyde is represented by the two resonance structures

$$^{\ominus}CH_2\!-\!CH\!=\!O \leftrightarrow CH_2\!=\!CH\!-\!O^{\ominus}$$

indicating a high electron density on the α-carbon atom *and* on the oxygen atom. Although the major contributing structure to the resonance hybrid is, in fact, the oxanion, the entity reacts with carbonyl compounds in most instances as a carbanion. This is a consequence of the advantageous bond energies that the product derives from C—C bond formation as compared with C—O bond formation, illustrated in Fig. 4-23. In the majority of reactions involving active methylene intermediates, the strength of bonding in the product is the determining feature, and as a consequence it is the carbon portion of the ambident anion which reacts in spite of the fact that this is the less electron-rich center. In a few cases, however, the reaction is sensitive to the concentration of negative charge in the ambident anion and not responsive to the bond strengths in the product. In this situation the reaction occurs at the hetero atom center of the ambident anion.

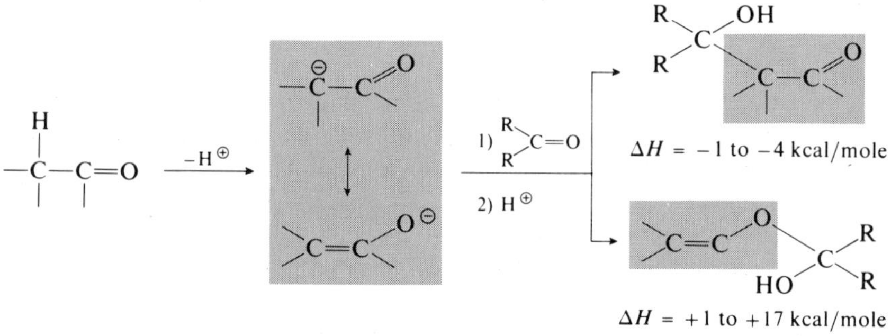

Fig. 4-23 Heats of reaction for active methylene carbanions reacting at oxygen and carbon end of ambident anion.

The reactions between active methylene carbanions and carbonyl compounds are known as (a) "aldol condensations," when the first step in the process is direct addition to an aldehyde or ketone; (b) "Michael reactions," when the process is conjugate addition; and (c) "Claisen condensations," when the addition-elimination route is followed. The mechanisms by which these reactions take place are identical with those that have already been discussed for direct addition, conjugate addition, and addition-elimination for other types of nucleophiles. Because of the variety of active methylene compounds and the variety of aldehydes, ketones, and carboxylic acid derivatives available, a large number of condensation reactions are known, and only a limited sampling can be discussed in this chapter.

The simplest example of the aldol condensation is the reaction in which acetaldehyde serves both as the active methylene component and as the carbonyl component (see Fig. 4-24). The equilibrium constant for

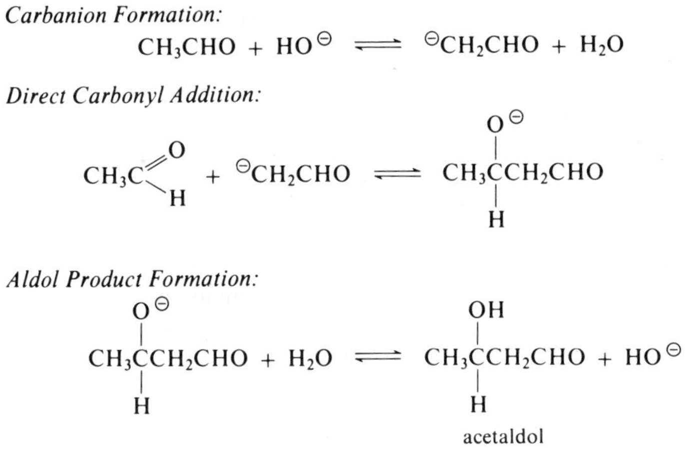

Carbanion Formation:
$$CH_3CHO + HO^\ominus \rightleftharpoons {}^\ominus CH_2CHO + H_2O$$

Direct Carbonyl Addition:

$$CH_3C{\overset{O}{\underset{H}{<}}} + {}^\ominus CH_2CHO \rightleftharpoons CH_3\overset{O^\ominus}{\underset{H}{\overset{|}{C}}}CH_2CHO$$

Aldol Product Formation:

$$CH_3\overset{O^\ominus}{\underset{H}{\overset{|}{C}}}CH_2CHO + H_2O \rightleftharpoons CH_3\overset{OH}{\underset{H}{\overset{|}{C}}}CH_2CHO + HO^\ominus$$

acetaldol

Fig. 4-24 Self-condensation reaction of acetaldehyde.

the process favors the forward step, and acetaldol can be obtained in good yield. In common with other direct carbonyl additions, however, the aldol condensation is strongly susceptible to steric hindrance. While most aldehydes of the structure RCH_2CHO readily self-condense, ketone condensations are much less likely to proceed in good yield. Acetone, for instance, furnishes only 2% of diacetone alcohol in the equilibrium mixture. To obtain this product in useful amounts requires special measures which make use of selective product removal to shift the equilibrium. This has been accomplished in a clever way by carrying out the reaction in the apparatus pictured in Fig. 4-25. Acetone, contained in the round bottomed flask, is heated to boiling and condensed, and the condensate passes back into the flask by way of a porous thimble filled with barium hydroxide. In the presence of this base, the aldol condensation proceeds to form a small amount of diacetone alcohol. Since diacetone alcohol is much higher boiling than acetone, once it has passed through the porous cup it runs back into the boiling flask where it remains unchanged, unable in the absence of a basic catalyst to revert to acetone. Thus, only acetone continues to vaporize, condense, and contact the catalyst; as a result, it is converted almost entirely to condensation product.

Mixed aldol condensations between different aldehydes or between aldehydes and ketones are generally unsatisfactory because of the com-

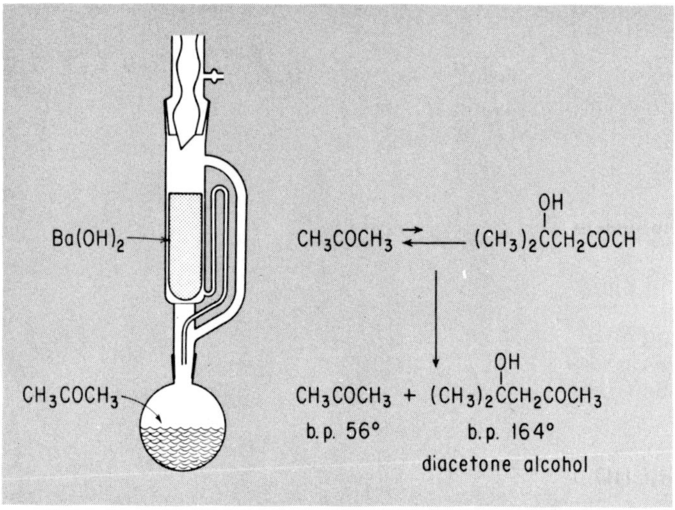

Ba(OH)₂

$$CH_3COCH_3 \rightleftarrows (CH_3)_2\overset{\overset{OH}{|}}{C}CH_2COCH$$

CH₃COCH₃

$$CH_3COCH_3 + (CH_3)_2\overset{\overset{OH}{|}}{C}CH_2COCH_3$$
b.p. 56°   b.p. 164°
diacetone alcohol

Fig. 4-25 Self-condensation reaction of acetone.

plexity of the product mixture. Only in exceptional cases, where one reactant is the more effective active methylene component and the other reactant is the more reactive carbonyl component, is the reaction useful as, for instance, in the condensation of dihydroxyacetone and glyceraldehyde to form fructose and sorbose (Fig. 4-26).

Mixed aldol condensations involving active methylene compounds which cannot self-condense are frequently useful. Nitromethane, for instance, is a particularly reactive compound and condenses readily with aldehydes and ketones to form nitro alcohols. These are good synthesis intermediates, as illustrated by the reactions shown in Fig. 4-27.

As has already been observed in the case of the self condensation of acetone, the equilibrium may not favor the aldol product. In such instances it is necessary either to resort to selective product removal (e.g.,

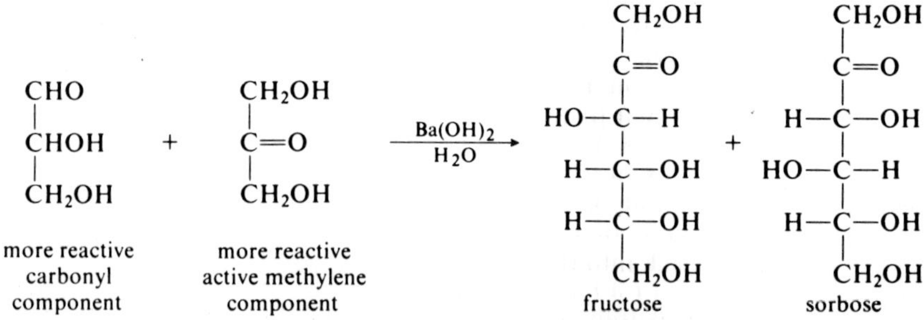

$$
\begin{array}{c}
\text{CHO} \\
| \\
\text{CHOH} \\
| \\
\text{CH}_2\text{OH} \\
\end{array}
\;+\;
\begin{array}{c}
\text{CH}_2\text{OH} \\
| \\
\text{C}=\text{O} \\
| \\
\text{CH}_2\text{OH} \\
\end{array}
\;\xrightarrow[\text{H}_2\text{O}]{\text{Ba(OH)}_2}\;
\begin{array}{c}
\text{CH}_2\text{OH} \\
| \\
\text{C}=\text{O} \\
| \\
\text{HO}-\text{C}-\text{H} \\
| \\
\text{H}-\text{C}-\text{OH} \\
| \\
\text{H}-\text{C}-\text{OH} \\
| \\
\text{CH}_2\text{OH} \\
\end{array}
\;+\;
\begin{array}{c}
\text{CH}_2\text{OH} \\
| \\
\text{C}=\text{O} \\
| \\
\text{H}-\text{C}-\text{OH} \\
| \\
\text{HO}-\text{C}-\text{H} \\
| \\
\text{H}-\text{C}-\text{OH} \\
| \\
\text{CH}_2\text{OH} \\
\end{array}
$$

more reactive   more reactive   fructose   sorbose
carbonyl   active methylene
component   component

Fig. 4-26 Synthesis of fructose and sorbose via aldol condensation.

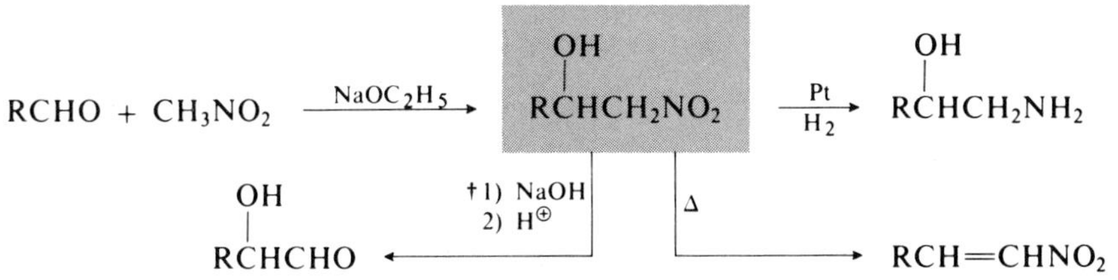

$$RCHO + CH_3NO_2 \xrightarrow{NaOC_2H_5} \underset{\underset{RCHCH_2NO_2}{|}}{OH} \xrightarrow[H_2]{Pt} \underset{\underset{RCHCH_2NH_2}{|}}{OH}$$

$$\underset{\underset{RCHCHO}{|}}{OH} \xleftarrow[\substack{2) \ H^{\oplus}}]{\dagger 1) \ NaOH} \qquad \xrightarrow{\Delta} \qquad RCH{=}CHNO_2$$

Fig. 4-27 Preparation and conversions of β-nitroalcohols.

Fig. 4-25) or to chemical conversion of the aldol product. The most usual of the latter devices is to carry out the reaction under conditions which favor an exothermic dehydration reaction (compare with addition reactions of hetero atom nucleophiles, Sec. 3.2). For instance, benzaldehyde (incapable of self-condensation) reacts with acetaldehyde in the presence of base to furnish cinnamaldehyde in good yield, a result of the sequence of reactions shown in Fig. 4-28. A number of related addition-dehydration reactions are known and are usually designated by the names of the men who discovered or developed them. Several such examples are illustrated in Fig. 4-29.

Formaldehyde, an extremely reactive carbonyl compound which cannot undergo self-condensation, engages in two types of reactions known as the "Tollens condensation" and the "Mannich reaction" (Fig. 4-30). The former is simply an example of a mixed aldol condensation; the latter is more complex in also involving an amine as a reactant. Mannich bases, the products of the Mannich reaction, are useful synthesis intermediates, particularly in the preparation of α,β-unsaturated carbonyl compounds.

Carbanions from active methylene compounds share, in common with other nucleophiles, the ability to undergo conjugate addition to activated double bonds (class AB, BB, and BC carbonyl compounds as well as the other species identified in Fig. 3-16 footnote), such reactions being classed as "Michael condensations." The varied selection of active methylene

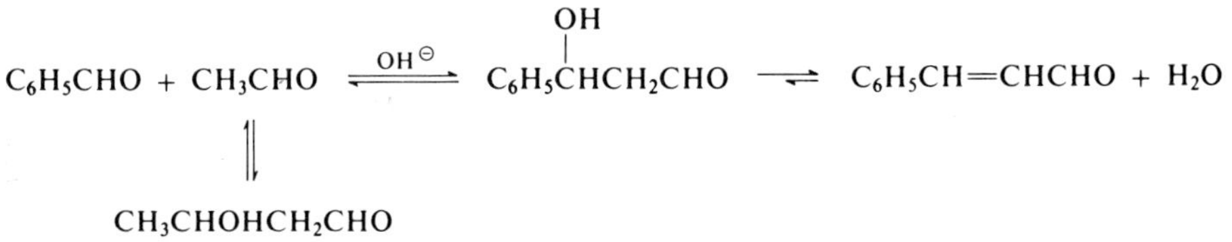

$$C_6H_5CHO + CH_3CHO \underset{}{\overset{OH^{\ominus}}{\rightleftharpoons}} \underset{\underset{C_6H_5CHCH_2CHO}{|}}{OH} \rightleftharpoons C_6H_5CH{=}CHCHO + H_2O$$

$$\updownarrow$$

$$CH_3CHOHCH_2CHO$$

Fig. 4-28 Claisen-Schmidt condensation of acetaldehyde and benzaldehyde.

† Treatment of RCH_2NO_2 with sodium hydroxide forms the sodium salt (i.e., $RCHNO_2^{\ominus} \ Na^{\oplus}$) which, upon addition to fairly concentrated sulfuric acid forms $RCHO$. The over-all process is called the Nef reaction and is one of the many excellent methods for preparing aldehydes and ketones.

Perkin Condensation: *Aromatic aldehydes with anhydrides in the presence of carboxylic acid salt.*

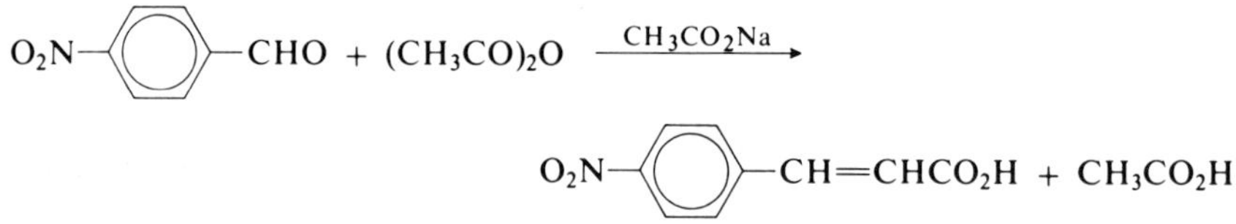

$$O_2N-\bigcirc-CHO + (CH_3CO)_2O \xrightarrow{CH_3CO_2Na}$$

$$O_2N-\bigcirc-CH=CHCO_2H + CH_3CO_2H$$

Knoevenagel Reaction: *Aliphatic and aromatic aldehydes with malonic acid or malonic esters in the presence of amines.*

$$CH_3CH=CHCHO + CH_2(CO_2H)_2 \xrightarrow{pyridine}$$
$$CH_3CH=CHCH=CHCO_2H + CO_2 + H_2O$$

Knoevenagel-Cope Reaction: *Aldehydes and ketones with cyanoacetic ester in the presence of acetamide in benzene solution (azeotropic removal of water formed in reaction).*

$$\begin{matrix} C_6H_5 \\ C_6H_5 \end{matrix}C=O + CH_2\begin{matrix} CN \\ CO_2C_2H_5 \end{matrix} \longrightarrow \begin{matrix} C_6H_5 \\ C_6H_5 \end{matrix}C=C\begin{matrix} CN \\ CO_2C_2H_5 \end{matrix} + H_2O$$

Stobbe-Johnson Condensation: *Aldehydes and ketones with succinic esters in the presence of potassium t-butoxide.*

$$\begin{matrix} CH_3 \\ CH_3 \end{matrix}C=O + \begin{matrix} CH_2CO_2CH_3 \\ | \\ CH_2CO_2CH_3 \end{matrix} \xrightarrow{(CH_3)_3COK} \begin{matrix} (CH_3)_2C=CCO_2CH_3 \\ | \\ CH_2CO_2H \end{matrix} + CH_3OH$$

Fig. 4-29 Aldol type addition-dehydration reactions.

Tollens Condensation:

$$HCHO + CH_3CH_2\overset{O}{\overset{\|}{C}}CH_2CH_3 \xrightarrow{Ca(OH)_2} \underset{CH_2OH}{\overset{CH_2OH}{CH_3C}}-\overset{O}{\overset{\|}{C}}-\underset{CH_2OH}{\overset{CH_2OH}{CCH_3}}$$

Mannich Reaction:

$$HCHO + C_6H_5COCH_3 + (CH_3)_2\dot{N}H \xrightarrow{HCl} C_6H_5COCH_2CH_2\dot{N}(CH_3)_2$$
a Mannich base

$$\downarrow \begin{matrix} 1) \ NaOH \\ 2) \ Heat \end{matrix}$$

$$C_6H_5COCH=CH_2 + (CH_3)_2NH$$

Fig. 4-30 Tollens condensation and Mannich reaction.

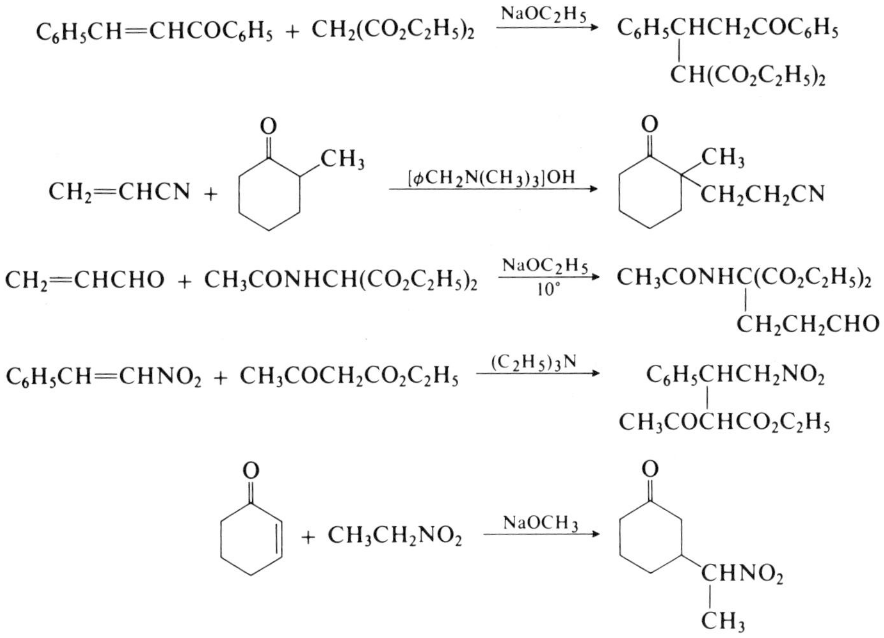
C6H5CH=CHCOC6H5 + CH2(CO2C2H5)2
NaOC2H5
C6H5CHCH2COC6H5
CH(CO2C2H5)2
CH2=CHCN +
CH3
[φCH2N(CH3)3]OH
CH2CH2CN
CH2=CHCHO + CH3CONHCH(CO2C2H5)2
NaOC2H5
10°
CH3CONHC(CO2C2H5)2
CH2CH2CHO
C6H5CH=CHNO2 + CH3COCH2CO2C2H5
(C2H5)3N
C6H5CHCH2NO2
CH3COCHCO2C2H5
+ CH3CH2NO2
NaOCH3
CHNO2
CH3

Fig. 4-31 Michael condensation reactions.

compounds and acceptor compounds makes many combinations possible. A few representative examples are shown in Fig. 4-31.

Carbanions from active methylene compounds also share, in common with many other nucleophiles, the ability to engage in addition-elimination reactions with carbonyl compounds. When the carbonyl compound is an ester, the reactions are called "Claisen condensations," the prototype for which is the self-condensation of ethyl acetate to produce acetoacetic ester (Fig. 4-32). The delocalization energy of one ester group (see Sec.

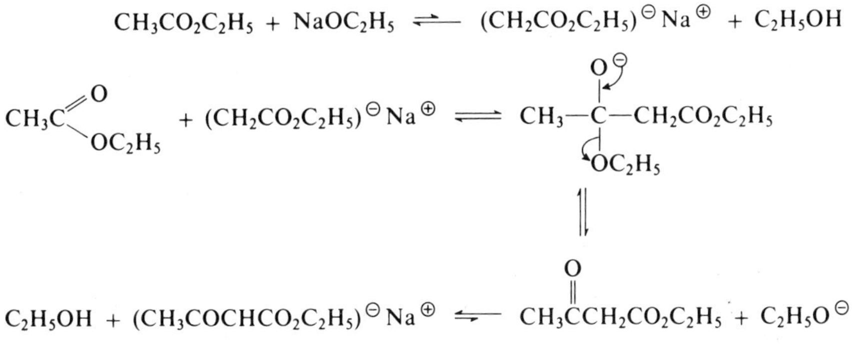
CH3CO2C2H5 + NaOC2H5 ⇌ (CH2CO2C2H5)⊖Na⊕ + C2H5OH
CH3C(=O)OC2H5 + (CH2CO2C2H5)⊖Na⊕ ⇌ CH3—C(O⊖)—CH2CO2C2H5
OC2H5
C2H5OH + (CH3COCHCO2C2H5)⊖Na⊕ ⇌ CH3CCH2CO2C2H5 + C2H5O⊖

Fig. 4-32 Self-condensation reaction of ethyl acetate.

1.8) is lost in going from ethyl acetate to acetoacetic ester, and this is not offset by the more favorable bond energies in the product. As a consequence, the reaction must be pushed either by removal of ethanol as it is formed (e.g., by distillation if it is the lowest-boiling component) or by the use of a full mole-equivalent of sodium ethoxide to convert acetoacetic ester to its enolate (i.e., acetoacetic ester is a stronger acid than ethanol). While the latter method suffices for esters having at least two α-hydrogens, it cannot operate for esters such as ethyl isobutyrate, for the β-keto ester that is formed in this case has no active methylene hydrogens. This problem has been circumvented by using the very strong base sodium triphenylmethyl, which converts more of the starting ester to the sodium enolate, thereby greatly increasing the equilibrium concentration of β-keto ester (Fig. 4-33).

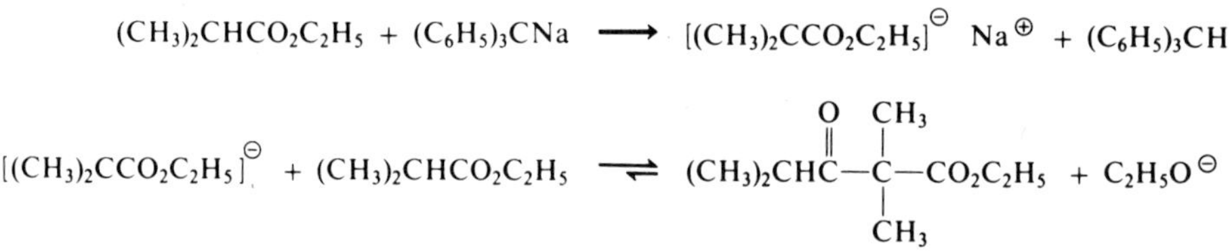

$$(CH_3)_2CHCO_2C_2H_5 + (C_6H_5)_3CNa \longrightarrow [(CH_3)_2CCO_2C_2H_5]^{\ominus} Na^{\oplus} + (C_6H_5)_3CH$$

$$[(CH_3)_2CCO_2C_2H_5]^{\ominus} + (CH_3)_2CHCO_2C_2H_5 \rightleftharpoons (CH_3)_2CHC\overset{\overset{\displaystyle O}{\|}}{-}\overset{\overset{\displaystyle CH_3}{|}}{\underset{\underset{\displaystyle CH_3}{|}}{C}}-CO_2C_2H_5 + C_2H_5O^{\ominus}$$

Fig. 4-33 Self-condensation of ethyl isobutyrate.

Mixed Claisen condensations, like mixed aldol condensations, generally give intractable mixtures, but they may be useful in certain cases where at least one of the reactants is a good carbonyl component incapable of self-condensation. For instance, ethyl formate and ethyl carbonate react in the fashion illustrated in Fig. 4-34. Other suitable esters include ethyl benzoate and diethyl oxalate.

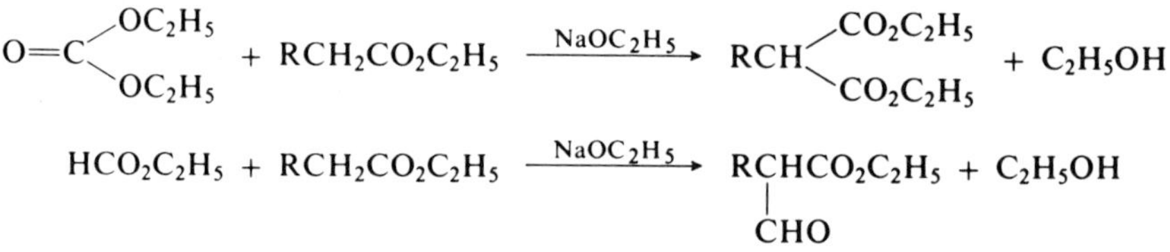

$$O{=}C\overset{\nearrow OC_2H_5}{\underset{\searrow OC_2H_5}{}} + RCH_2CO_2C_2H_5 \xrightarrow{NaOC_2H_5} RCH\overset{\nearrow CO_2C_2H_5}{\underset{\searrow CO_2C_2H_5}{}} + C_2H_5OH$$

$$HCO_2C_2H_5 + RCH_2CO_2C_2H_5 \xrightarrow{NaOC_2H_5} \underset{\underset{\displaystyle CHO}{|}}{RCH}CO_2C_2H_5 + C_2H_5OH$$

Fig. 4-34 Mixed Claisen condensations (ester-ester).

Active methylene compounds other than esters can also engage esters in mixed Claisen-type condensations, as illustrated in Fig. 4-35.

Mechanistically identical with the Claisen condensation (which involves esters) are the reactions of active methylene compounds with other class AC compounds, particularly acid chlorides. Acyl and aroyl groups

$$CH_3CO_2C_2H_5 + CH_3COCH_3 \xrightarrow{NaOC_2H_5} CH_3COCH_2COCH_3 + C_2H_5OH$$

$$C_6H_5CO_2C_2H_5 + C_6H_5COCH_3 \xrightarrow{NaOC_2H_5} C_6H_5COCH_2COC_6H_5 + C_2H_5OH$$

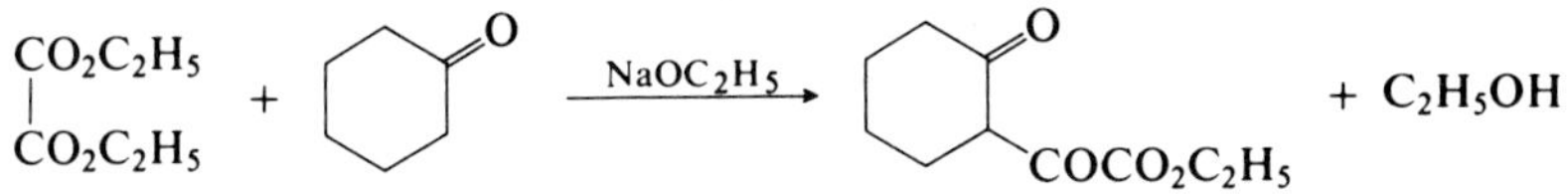

Fig. 4-35 Mixed Claisen-type condensations (ketone-ester).

can be introduced into active methylene compounds by reactions of the type illustrated in Fig. 4-36.

An example of a type Z addition-elimination reaction (see path *a* in Fig. 2-18) involving a carbon nucleophile is the glycidic ester condensation. When an α-halo ester is mixed with an active methylene compound in the presence of a base, a reaction takes place according to the scheme

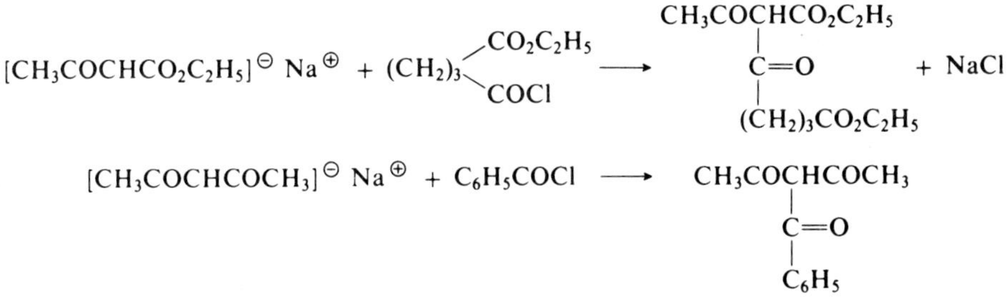

Fig. 4-36 Addition-elimination reactions with active methylene nucleophiles.

shown in Fig. 4-37 to produce an α,β-epoxy ester (a glycidic ester). The reaction affords a useful method for introducing a formyl group or a keto moiety at the site of a carbonyl group, for glycidic esters can be hydrolyzed and decarboxylated by the pathway shown in Fig. 5-17.

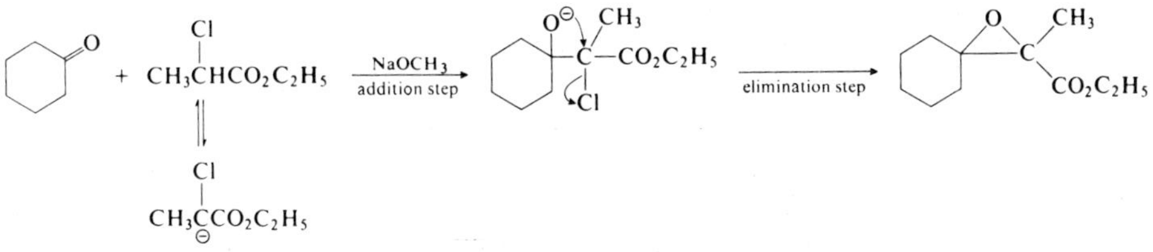

Fig. 4-37 Glycidic ester synthesis.

4.5 OTHER SOURCES OF CARBON NUCLEOPHILES

As discussed in Sec. 4.4, active methylene compounds can yield carbanions via α-proton abstraction by base. An alternative route involves the action of a metal on an α-halo carbonyl compound. This method has been most effectively applied in the case of α-halo esters and is known as the "Reformatsky reaction." When an aldehyde or ketone is mixed with an α-halo ester in the presence of zinc, a reaction takes place to yield a β-hydroxy ester, as illustrated by the first example in Fig. 4-38. The role of the zinc is to supply electrons to the carbonyl system, thereby converting it from an electron-poor (due to electron withdrawal by the halogen) to an electron-rich entity, i.e., a carbanion. The postulated intermediate is an organozinc compound which, being less nucleophilic than a Grignard reagent, shows much more selectivity between aldehydes or ketones and esters. The reaction also proceeds with vinylogs of α-halo esters, as illustrated by the second example in Fig. 4-38. Since the Reformatsky

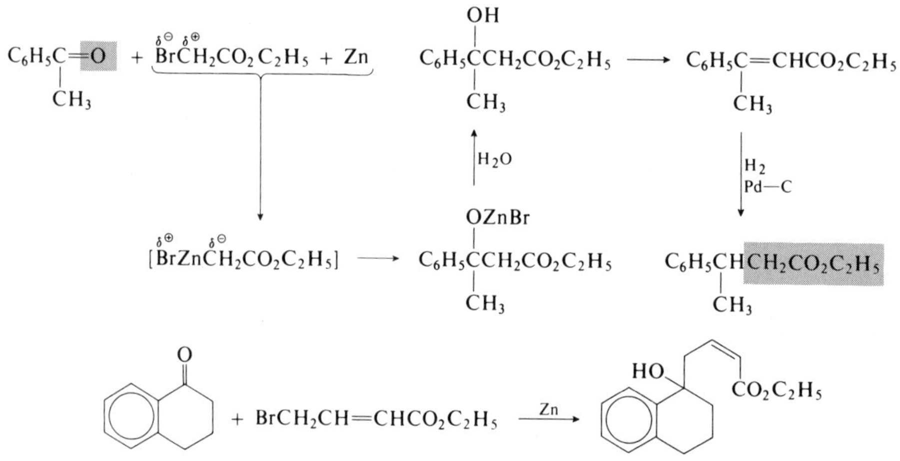

Fig. 4-38 The Reformatsky reaction.

reaction is not successful with β-halo esters, however, it seems reasonable to consider it a special example of an active methylene condensation reaction, although it might also be considered a special example of a Grignard-type addition reaction. β-Hydroxy esters, the products of Reformatsky reactions, are easily dehydrated to the α,β-unsaturated ester or the β,γ-unsaturated ester, the outcome depending on the structure of the reactants and the dehydrating agent used. Hydrogenation of either of the unsaturated esters yields the same saturated compound, however, and the over-all sequence provides a useful method for extending a carbon chain at the site of a carbonyl group.

An interesting example of a carbon nucleophile is observed in the benzoin condensation in which aromatic aldehydes and other non-enolizable aldehydes undergo a bimolecular reaction to yield α-hydroxy ketones. Only a few substances will catalyze the process, the simplest of these being cyanide ion. The role of the cyanide is thought to be to convert the aldehyde to the cyanohydrin, thereby labilizing the carbon-bound hydrogen via stabilization of the anion through charge delocalization to the nitrogen (i.e., $\text{Ar}\overset{\ominus}{\underset{\underset{\text{OH}}{|}}{\text{C}}}-C\equiv N \leftrightarrow \text{Ar}\underset{\underset{\text{OH}}{|}}{\text{C}}=C=\overset{\ominus}{N}$). The ensuing steps are illustrated in Fig. 4-39 and are postulated to involve the formation of a tetrahedral intermediate which subsequently collapses to the α-hydroxy ketone by expulsion of cyanide ion (reverse cyanohydrin reaction).

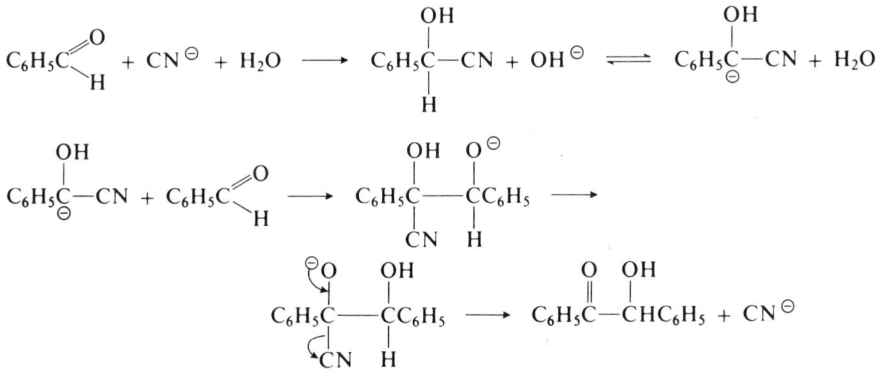

Fig. 4-39 The benzoin condensation of benzaldehyde.

Still other examples of carbon nucleophiles are observed in certain compounds containing two or three strongly electron-withdrawing groups attached to the same carbon atom. Chloroform, for instance, is acidic enough to form an anion and to condense with acetone to yield $Cl_3CC(CH_3)_2OH$.

4.6 POLYFUNCTIONAL CARBONYL COMPOUNDS (INTRAMOLECULAR REACTIONS)

If a carbon nucleophile is located in a molecule which also contains a carbonyl system, an intramolecular interaction is possible. For the reasons given in Sec. 3.7, this is most favorable when it leads to a product containing a five-membered or six-membered ring. Although only a very few examples are known (see first two reactions of Fig. 4-40) which involve $R_2C=Z$ type nucleophiles or organometallic reagents, there are

Diazoalkane-Ketone:

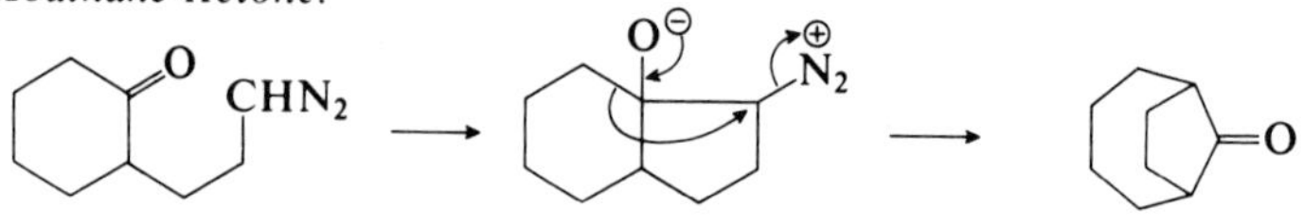
O
CHN₂
O⊖
⊕N₂
O

Grignard-Ketone:

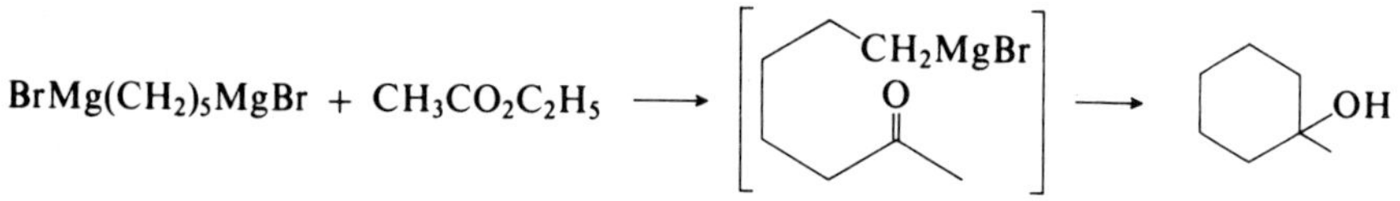
BrMg(CH₂)₅MgBr + CH₃CO₂C₂H₅
CH₂MgBr
O
OH

Aldol Condensation:

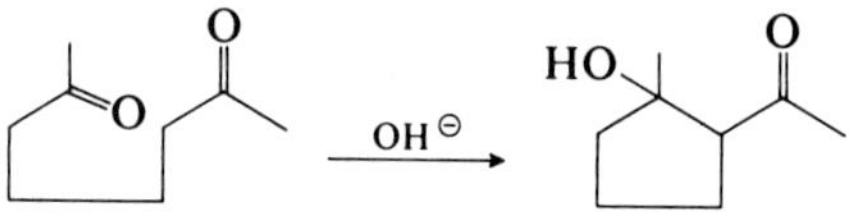
O
O
OH⊖
HO
O

Claisen Ester Condensation (Dieckmann Condensation):

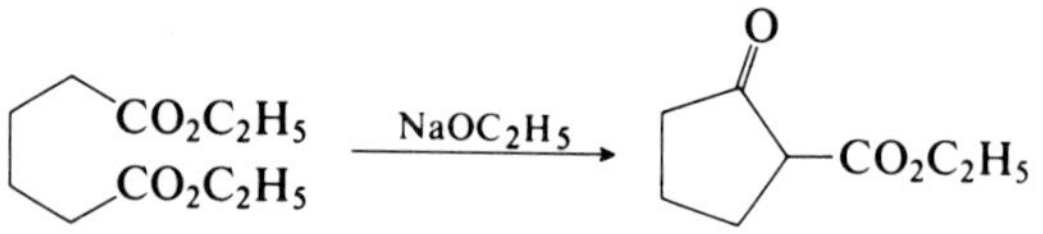
CO₂C₂H₅
CO₂C₂H₅
NaOC₂H₅
O
CO₂C₂H₅

Claisen Ketone Condensation:

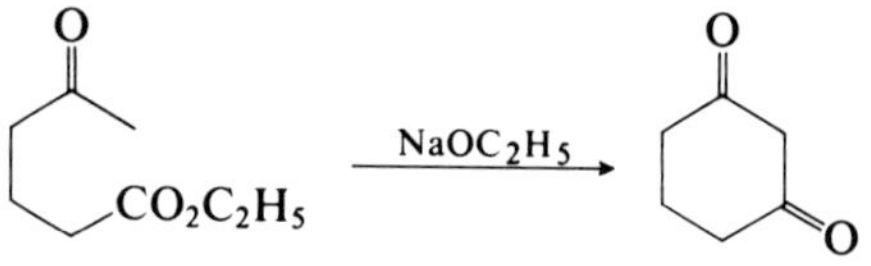
O
CO₂C₂H₅
NaOC₂H₅
O
O

Michael Condensation:

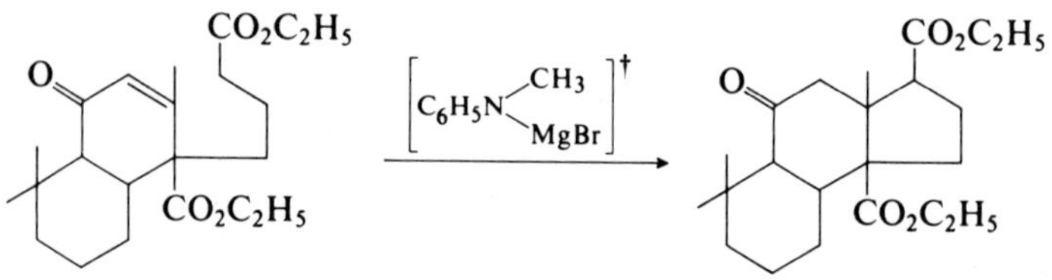
CO₂C₂H₅
O
CO₂C₂H₅
C₆H₅N CH₃ MgBr †
CO₂C₂H₅
O
CO₂C₂H₅

Fig. 4-40 Intramolecular reactions with carbon nucleophiles.

numerous examples which involve active methylene nucleophiles. Intramolecular aldol condensations and intramolecular Claisen condensations are exceedingly useful in the synthesis of carbocyclic compounds containing five-membered and six-membered rings and, under suitable conditions, can be used to prepare rings of larger size. Probably of greatest service is the intramolecular Claisen condensation of diesters, a process usually called the "Dieckmann condensation." The product from a

† This reagent acts as a base, comparable to $NaOC_2H_5$, to form the enolate.

Dieckmann condensation is a β-keto ester which frequently can be alkylated at the active methylene position, or hydrolyzed with dilute acid to a cycloalkanone, or hydrolyzed with strong base to a dibasic acid (see p. 61). The last four examples in Fig. 4-40 are illustrative of intramolecular reactions involving active methylene nucleophiles.

Interesting combinations of the types of reactions discussed in Chaps. 3 and 4 have been devised for the synthesis of various cyclic compounds.[†] Many heterocyclic syntheses combine hetero atom additions and active methylene additions in an intermolecular-intramolecular sequence. A typical example is the synthesis of the quinoline derivative illustrated by the first reaction in Fig. 4-41. A dramatic "one-flask" synthesis of a tropinone derivative, illustrated by the second reaction in Fig. 4-41, involves the interaction of succindialdehyde, diethyl β-ketoglutarate, and methylamine. The reaction can be interpreted as a combination of intermolecular and intramolecular aldol condensations and hetero atom conjugate additions. An extremely useful reaction, known as the "Robinson Mannich base synthesis" and illustrated by the third example of Fig. 4-41,

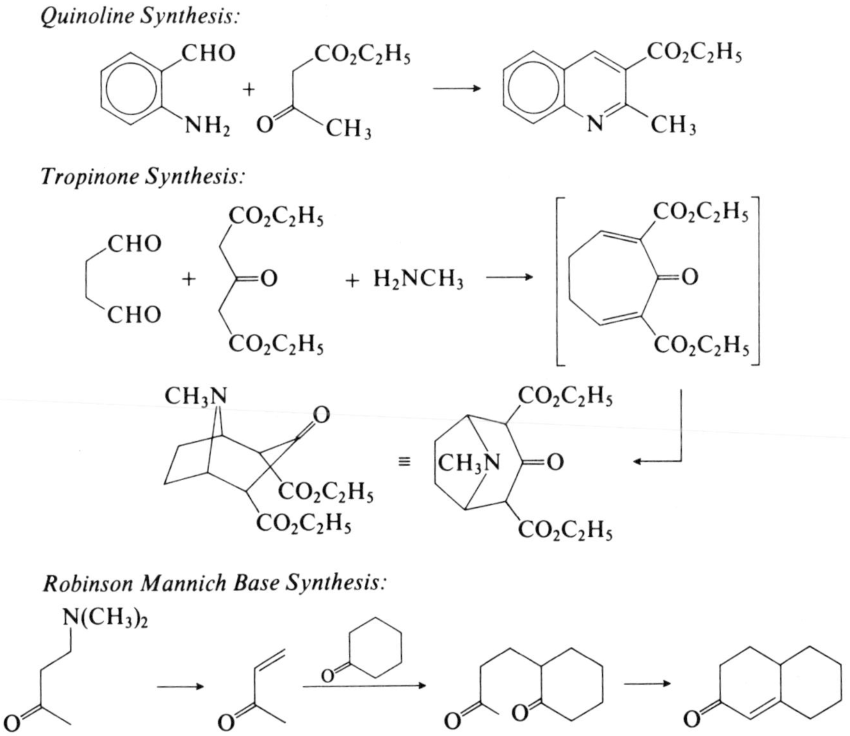

Quinoline Synthesis:

Tropinone Synthesis:

Robinson Mannich Base Synthesis:

Fig. 4-41 Synthesis of cyclic compounds via combination reactions.

[†] For additional details see R. E. Ireland, *op. cit.*

involves the interaction of a β-amino ketone (a Mannich base; see Fig. 4-30) with a cyclic ketone. The reaction is interpreted as involving a base-catalyzed conversion of the Mannich base to an α,β-unsaturated ketone, a Michael condensation between the cyclic ketone and the α,β-unsaturated ketone, and an intramolecular addition-dehydration reaction.

Those readers who have completed the laborious journey through Chaps. 3 and 4 are now reminded of the suggestion in Sec. 1.4, namely, that the *vusillus* route[†] be employed by going back to Chap. 2.

PROBLEMS

1. Starting with chemicals available for less than $10 per 100 g, devise syntheses for the following compounds:

a.

b. $Cl-$⟨⟩$-COCH_2CH_2N\overset{CH_3}{\underset{\phi}{\diagdown}}$

c. $CH_3CH_2CH_2CH_2\underset{\underset{\text{(naphthyl)}}{|}}{\overset{\overset{OH}{|}}{C}}CH_2CH_3$

d. $\phi CH_2\overset{\overset{O}{||}}{C}\underset{\underset{\phi}{|}}{CH}CO_2C_2H_5$

e. $CH_3\underset{\underset{CH_2CH=CH_2}{|}}{\overset{\overset{OH}{|}}{C}}CH_2CH=CH_2$

f.

g. $\left(CH_3O-⟨⟩-\right)_3COH$

h.

i. $\phi\overset{\overset{O}{||}}{C}\underset{\underset{CH_3}{|}}{C}(CH_2CH_2CN)_2$

j.

2. Indicate the reaction or reactions that might be employed to effect the following conversions:

a.

b.

[†] For further details concerning the *vusillus* route see A. A. Milnei, *Winnie Ille Pu* (New York: E. P. Dutton & Co., Inc, 1960) p. 23.

c. $C_6H_5CO_2H \longrightarrow C_6H_5COCH_2Br$

d. $(C_6H_5)_2C=O \longrightarrow (C_6H_5)_2CHOHCH_2NH_2$ (via two methods)

e.

f.

g. $C_6H_5CH=CHCO_2H \longrightarrow C_6H_5CH=CHCOCH(CH_3)_2$ (via several methods)

h.

i.

j.

3. Answer the following questions:

a. D-Glyceraldehyde reacts with dihydroxyacetone to yield D-fructose and D-sorbose (see Fig. 4-26). Would any other D-2-ketohexoses be expected as products? If DL-glyceraldehyde were employed, how many stereo-isomers might be present in the reaction mixture?

b. The conversion RCHO → RCH=CHR' can be effected via a Grignard reaction followed by dehydration or via a Wittig reaction. What advantage might the latter method have in the general case?

c. Unless excess diazomethane is used in the conversion of carboxylic acid chlorides to diazoketones, the product is the α-chloroketone, e.g., RCOCl → RCOCH$_2$Cl. What is the reason for this?

d. Why is the conversion of 2-methoxytropone to 2-methyltropone (see last example of Fig. 4-17) classed as a 1,8-conjugate addition?

e. Explain why benzoquinone reacts more readily with HCl via conjugate addition than does methyl vinyl ketone.

f. Several mechanisms have been suggested for the Mannich condensation (see Fig. 4-30), including the two illustrated below. What experiments might be designed to allow a distinction between these two mechanisms?

(i) $RCOCH_2 + HCHO \rightarrow RCOC=CH_2$

$RCOC=CH_2 + R_2NH \rightarrow RCOCHCH_2NR_2$

(ii) $R_2NH + HCHO \rightarrow R_2NCH_2OH \rightarrow R_2\overset{\oplus}{N}=CH_2 + OH^{\ominus}$

$R_2\overset{\oplus}{N}=CH_2 + RCOCH \rightarrow RCOC-CH_2NR_2 + H^{\oplus}$

g. Outline the sequence of reactions that must take place in the base-catalyzed reaction between benzaldehyde and acetoacetic ester which yields 3-methyl-4,6-dicarbethoxy-5-phenyl-2-cyclohexenone.

h. The reaction of mesityl oxide with deoxybenzoin ($C_6H_5CH_2COC_6H_5$) yields the expected Michael addition product along with 3,4-diphenyl-5,5-dimethyl-2-cyclohexenone. What is the expected product and how can the formation of the cyclic product be explained?

i. The product resulting from the intramolecular Michael reaction illustrated in Fig. 4-40 can also be obtained from the sodium amide-catalyzed reaction of 1-acetyl-6,6-dimethylcyclohexene and 3,6-dicarbethoxy-2-hexanone. What are the reactions involved?

j. Acetylcyanide (CH_3COCN) yields $CH_3CO_2C(CN)_2CH_3$ when treated with potassium cyanide. Rationalize this reaction.

k. Ethyl crotonate and diethyl methylmalonate undergo a sodium ethoxide-catalyzed reaction to yield 1,1,3-tricarbethoxy-2-methylbutane. What would have been the expected product ("normal product"), and how can the formation of the "abnormal product" be explained?

SELECTED REFERENCES

Many additional examples of the types of reactions discussed in this chapter are to be found in (a) R. C. Fuson, *Reactions of Organic Compounds: A Textbook for the Advanced Student,* New York: John Wiley & Sons, Inc., 1962; (b) E. E. Royals, *Advanced Organic Chemistry,* Englewood Cliffs, N.J.: Prentice-Hall, Inc., 1956; (c) H. O. House, *Modern Synthetic Reactions,* New York: W. A. Benjamin, Inc., 1965; (d) E. Muller (ed.), *Methoden der Organischen Chemie (Houben-Weyl),* Stuttgart: Georg Thieme Verlag, Vols. 6–8 (1952–1965). Detailed discussions of certain of the topics covered in this chapter are to be found in (a) M. S. Kharasch and O. Reinmuth, *Grignard Reactions of Nonmetallic Substances,* Englewood Cliffs, N.J.: Prentice-Hall, Inc., 1954; (b) A. Maercker, "The Wittig Reaction," *Organic Reactions,* Vol. 14, p. 270 (1964); (c) C. D. Gutsche, "Diazoalkane-Carbonyl Reactions," *Organic Reactions,* Vol. 8, p. 364 (1954); (d) W. S. Johnson and G. H. Daub, "The Stobbe Condensation," *Organic Reactions,* Vol. 6, p. 1

(1951); (e) M. S. Newman and B. J. Magerlein, "The Glycidic Ester Condensation," *Organic Reactions,* Vol. 5, p. 413 (1949); (f) F. F. Blicke, "The Mannich Reaction," *Organic Reactions,* Vol. 1, p. 303 (1942); (g) C. R. Hauser and B. E. Hudson, "The Acetoacetic Ester Condensation," *Organic Reactions,* Vol. 1, p. 266 (1942); (h) J. R. Johnson, "The Perkin Reaction," *Organic Reactions,* Vol. 1, p. 210 (1942); (i) W. E. Bachmann and W. S. Struve, "The Arndt-Eistert Synthesis," *Organic Reactions,* Vol. 1, p. 38 (1942); (j) R. L. Shriner, "The Reformatsky Reaction," *Organic Reactions,* Vol. 1, p. 1 (1942); (k) N. O. V. Sonntag, "Reactions of Aliphatic Acid Chlorides," *Chem. Rev.,* **52**, 237 (1953).

5

Electrophilic Displacement Reactions with Carbonyl Compounds

5.1 INTRODUCTION

Reactions classed as nucleophilic may also be classed as electrophilic, the choice being determined by that part of the molecule on which one chooses to focus his attention. In the formation of a cyanohydrin, for instance, the reaction is viewed as either a nucleophilic displacement (or addition†) from the standpoint of the carbon of the carbonyl group (cyanide ion is the nucleophile) or as an electrophilic displacement (or addition†) from the standpoint of the oxygen of the carbonyl group (proton is the electrophile). In the majority of reactions discussed in Chaps. 3 and 4, the focus has been on the step in which the nucleophilic reagent combines with the carbonyl carbon. In some instances, however, attention is better directed to a preceding step, namely, the electrophilic displacement on oxygen by a proton or a Lewis acid. Such reactions include the acid-catalyzed hydration of aldehydes (see Fig. 2-3), acid-catalyzed aldol condensations, acid-catalyzed carbonyl addition reactions, acid-catalyzed addition-elimination reactions, and the Friedel-Crafts acylation reaction.

5.2 ACID-CATALYZED REACTIONS AT THE CARBONYL GROUP

The acid-catalyzed aldol condensation probably proceeds via the enol form, as depicted in Fig. 5-1. Unlike its base-catalyzed counterpart, however, the initially formed β-hydroxy compound is rarely isolable but rapidly undergoes acid-catalyzed dehydration to the α,β-unsaturated aldehyde or ketone. Further condensation frequently occurs with the incorporation of more than two molecules of the starting aldehyde or

† See Sec. 2.1 for comments on the terms "displacement" and "addition."

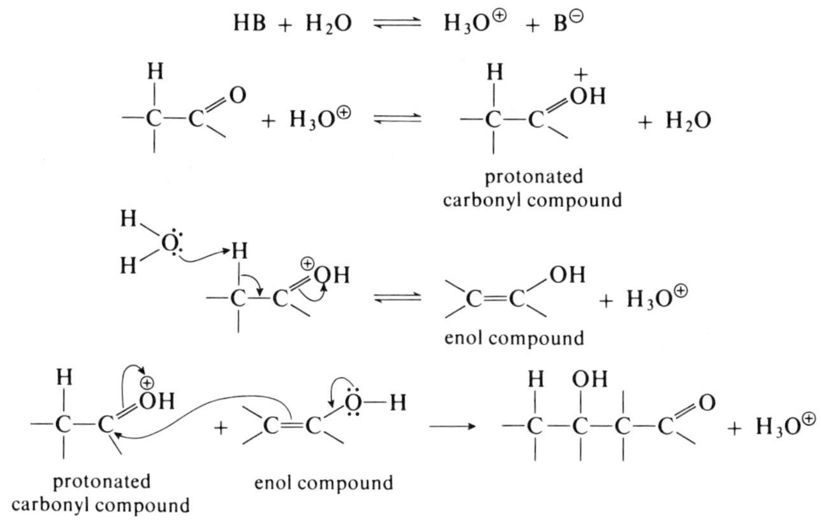

Fig. 5-1 Acid-catalyzed aldol condensation in aqueous solution.

ketone in the final product. Thus, acetone in the presence of hydrogen chloride yields mesityl oxide and phorone, and acetone in the presence of concentrated sulfuric acid yields mesitylene. Similarly, cyclohexanone with hydrogen chloride yields cyclohexylcyclohexenone, and cyclohexanone with concentrated sulfuric acid yields the aromatic compound corresponding to mesitylene, as illustrated in Fig. 5-2.

Under neutral or basic conditions no interaction of olefins or unactivated aromatic compounds with aldehydes or ketones occurs, because

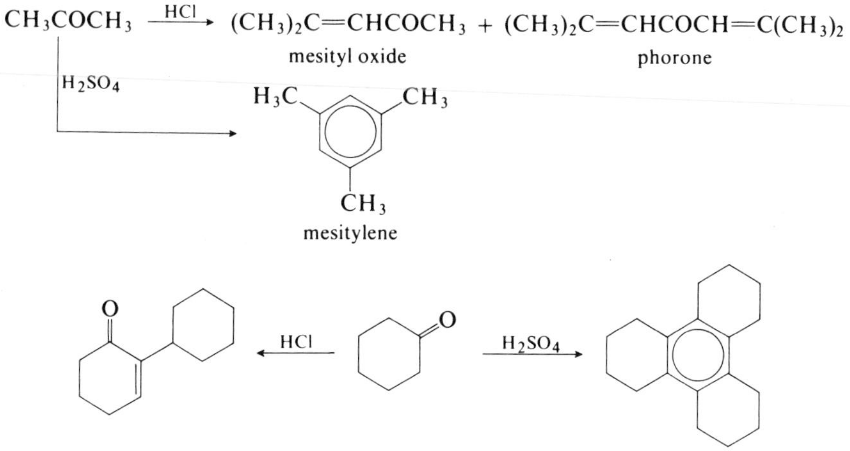

Fig. 5-2 Acid-catalyzed condensation of acetone and cyclohexanone.

the carbon-carbon pi bond is too weak a nucleophile to promote reaction with the carbonyl group. If, however, the carbonyl group is activated via interaction with a proton acid or Lewis acid, then a reaction may ensue, and with class AA compounds direct carbonyl addition reactions may be effected. For instance, formaldehyde can be added under acid-catalyzed conditions to olefinic bonds (Prins reaction) or to aromatic rings, as illustrated in Fig. 5-3.

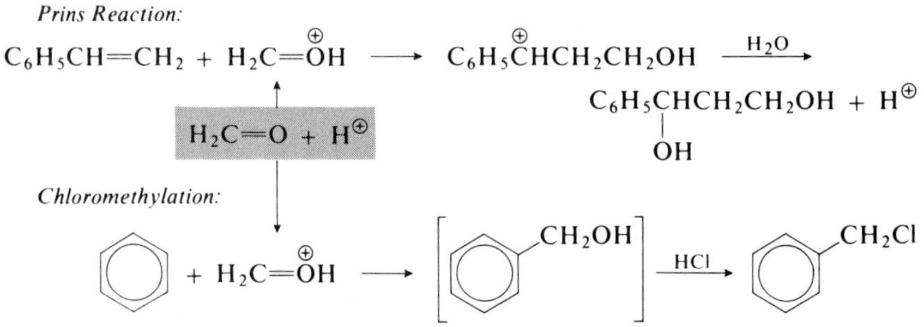

Prins Reaction:

$$C_6H_5CH{=}CH_2 + H_2C{=}\overset{\oplus}{O}H \longrightarrow C_6H_5\overset{\oplus}{C}HCH_2CH_2OH \xrightarrow{\;H_2O\;}$$

$$C_6H_5CHCH_2CH_2OH + H^{\oplus}$$
$$\underset{\textstyle OH}{|}$$

$$\uparrow$$

$$\boxed{H_2C{=}O + H^{\oplus}}$$

Chloromethylation:

$$\bigcirc + H_2C{=}\overset{\oplus}{O}H \longrightarrow \left[\bigcirc\!\!-\!CH_2OH \right] \xrightarrow{\;HCl\;} \bigcirc\!\!-\!CH_2Cl$$

Fig. 5-3 Acid-catalyzed reactions of formaldehyde.

Class AC compounds, particularly acid chlorides and anhydrides, may undergo acid-catalyzed addition-elimination reactions with olefins or aromatic nuclei, such reactions being classed as Friedel-Crafts acylations.[†] The function of the acid catalyst is to form a complex with the carbonyl compound (see Sec. 1.12), thereby increasing the electrophilic character of the carbonyl carbon. In certain instances (e.g., aluminum chloride with an acid chloride) the complex partly dissociates to an acylium cation and an aluminate anion, and it is the acylium cation which is thought, in many cases, to be the species which interacts with the aromatic nucleus, as illustrated in Fig. 5-4. The Friedel-Crafts acylation reaction is a most

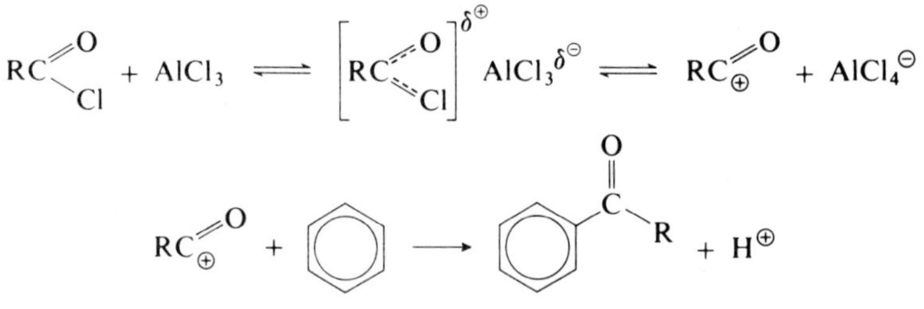

$$RC\!\!\underset{Cl}{\overset{O}{\diagdown}} + AlCl_3 \rightleftharpoons \left[RC\!\!\underset{Cl}{\overset{O}{\diagdown}} \right]^{\delta\oplus} AlCl_3^{\delta\ominus} \rightleftharpoons RC\!\!\underset{\oplus}{\overset{O}{\diagdown}} + AlCl_4^{\ominus}$$

$$RC\!\!\underset{\oplus}{\overset{O}{\diagdown}} + \bigcirc \longrightarrow \bigcirc\!\!\overset{\overset{O}{\|}}{\underset{}{C}}\!\!\diagdown_R + H^{\oplus}$$

Fig. 5-4 Friedel-Crafts acylation reaction.

† For a detailed discussion of this and related reactions see L. M. Stock, *Aromatic Substitution Reactions* (Englewood Cliffs, N.J.: Prentice-Hall, Inc., 1966).

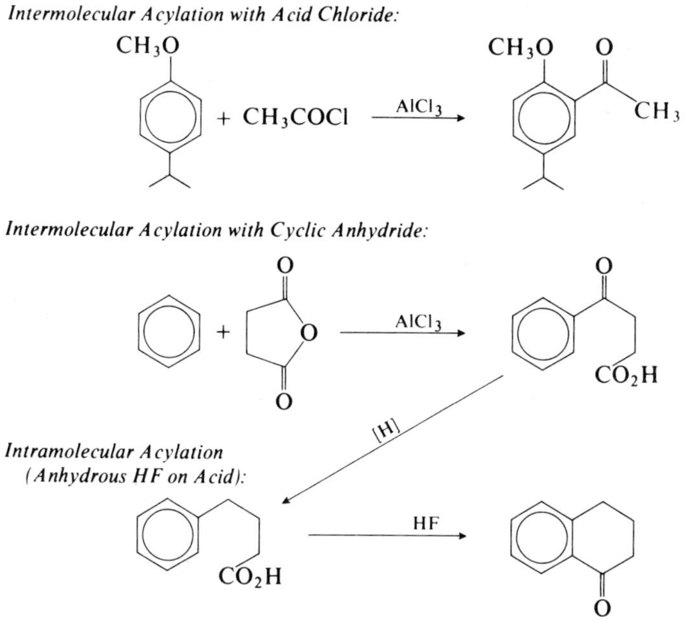

Intermolecular Acylation with Acid Chloride:

Intermolecular Acylation with Cyclic Anhydride:

Intramolecular Acylation (Anhydrous HF on Acid):

Fig. 5-5 Friedel-Crafts acylation reactions.

useful synthesis method, several examples of which are illustrated in Fig. 5-5.

5.3 ELECTROPHILIC DISPLACEMENTS AT α-POSITION OF CARBONYL COMPOUNDS

The acidity of compounds of the structure $H\!-\!Y\!-\!\overset{|}{C}\!=\!O$ has been discussed in Sec. 1.12. The anions formed by the action of base on these compounds can act as nucleophilic displacing agents toward a variety of reagents, the overall result being the replacement of H in $H\!-\!Y\!-\!\overset{|}{C}\!=\!O$ by some other atom or group. From the standpoint of the Y group, therefore, this sequence represents an electrophilic displacement, e.g., $H\!-\!Y\!-\!\overset{|}{C}\!=\!O \rightarrow Z\!-\!Y\!-\!\overset{|}{C}\!=\!O$. The displacement may occur intermolecularly with such reagents as alkyl halides (alkylation), class AC carbonyl compounds (acylation), halogens (halogenation), etc., or it may occur intramolecularly by processes which result in dehydrohalogenation, decarboxylation, etc.

The reaction of the anion from $H\!-\!Y\!-\!\overset{|}{C}\!=\!O$ with an alkyl halide is, from the standpoint of the alkyl halide, an S_N2 reaction and is susceptible to the various limitations of such reactions.[†] Thus, primary halides usually react readily, secondary halides with moderate facility, and tertiary halides very poorly. Esters of primary alcohols can be prepared, for instance, by the interaction of a carboxylate ion (Y = oxygen) with an alkyl halide. Since the carboxylate anion is particularly stable, it is not a strong nucleophile, and the silver salt of the acid is frequently used to drive the alkylation reaction. The probable function of the silver is to act as a Lewis acid in assisting the departure of the halogen atom from the alkyl halide. An alternative to this procedure is to use a diazoalkane as the alkylating agent. Diazoalkanes are sufficiently basic to accept a proton from a carboxylic acid; the diazonium ion thereby formed is exceedingly susceptible to displacement, and the result, as shown in Fig. 5-6, is the formation of the ester.

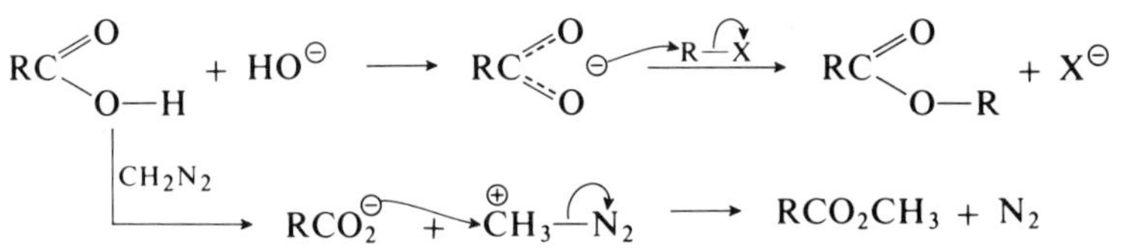

Fig. 5-6 Alkylation of carboxylate anion.

In $H-Y-\overset{|}{C}=O$ compounds with Y = nitrogen or carbon a new complication arises, namely, the anions are ambident and can undergo alkylation either at the Y atom or the O atom (see p. 83). For instance, as illustrated in Fig. 5-7, N-phenylformanilide treated with sodium ethoxide and ethyl iodide yields N-ethyl-N-phenylformanilide, while caprolactam reacts with dimethyl sulfate in the absence of alkali to yield the O-methyl compound. Similarly, active methylene compounds can undergo alkylation either at the α-carbon atom (C-alkylation) or at the

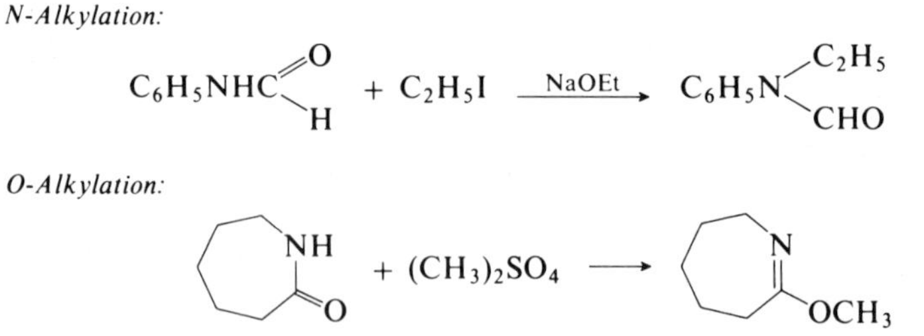

N-Alkylation:

O-Alkylation:

Fig. 5-7 N-Alkylation and O-alkylation of amides.

† W. H. Saunders, Jr., *op. cit.*

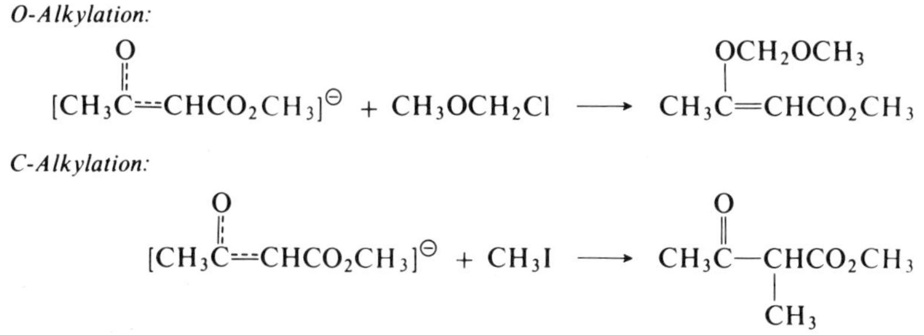

O-Alkylation:

$$[CH_3\overset{\overset{\displaystyle O}{\|}}{C}{=\!=\!=}CHCO_2CH_3]^{\ominus} + CH_3OCH_2Cl \longrightarrow CH_3\overset{\overset{\displaystyle OCH_2OCH_3}{|}}{C}{=}CHCO_2CH_3$$

C-Alkylation:

$$[CH_3\overset{\overset{\displaystyle O}{\|}}{C}{=\!=\!=}CHCO_2CH_3]^{\ominus} + CH_3I \longrightarrow CH_3\overset{\overset{\displaystyle O}{\|}}{C}-\underset{\underset{\displaystyle CH_3}{|}}{C}HCO_2CH_3$$

Fig. 5-8 C-Alkylation and O-alkylation of acetoacetic ester.

oxygen atom (O-alkylation). For example, the anion from acetoacetic ester yields the C-methyl compound or the O-methyl compound, depending upon the particular alkyl halide used, as shown in Fig. 5-8.

Although the reaction of an active methylene anion, $\left[\overset{\diagup}{\underset{\diagdown}{C}}-\overset{|}{C}{=}O\right]^{\ominus}$,

to form C-alkyl product or O-alkyl product is exothermic in both cases, the C-alkyl product is the thermodynamically more stable structure (see Fig. 4-23). Consequently, to the extent that bond formation has progressed in the transition states of the reactions of anion to product, the relative stabilities of the C-alkyl and O-alkyl products will be reflected in the ease with which the respective transition states are attained. With the majority of alkylating agents, a considerable displacement of the R—X bond is required to achieve the transition state, which is to say that a considerable amount of bonding between R and the ambident anion is necessary. In these cases, then, the outcome is C-alkylation. With more reactive alkylating agents such as chloromethyl ether, however, a milder nudge is required to expel the X group, which means that less bonding between R and the ambident anion is required to reach the transition state. In this case the stability of the final product is not sensed in the transition state, and the reaction takes place instead at the center of higher electron density in the ambident anion, which leads to O-alkylation (see p. 33–34).

The alkylation of active methylene compounds is a very useful synthesis method. It is best illustrated by the malonic ester synthesis and the acetoacetic ester synthesis, examples of which are shown in Fig. 5-9. Both procedures provide methods for the preparation of acids of the general structure $RR'CHCO_2H$ (malonic ester procedure generally preferred), while the acetoacetic ester procedure also provides a method for the preparation of ketones of the general structure $RR'CHCOCH_3$. Following the alkylation step, the sequences involve a hydrolysis step (see Fig. 3-27) and a decarboxylation step (see Fig. 5-17).

Although most of the examples of alkylation reactions involve doubly

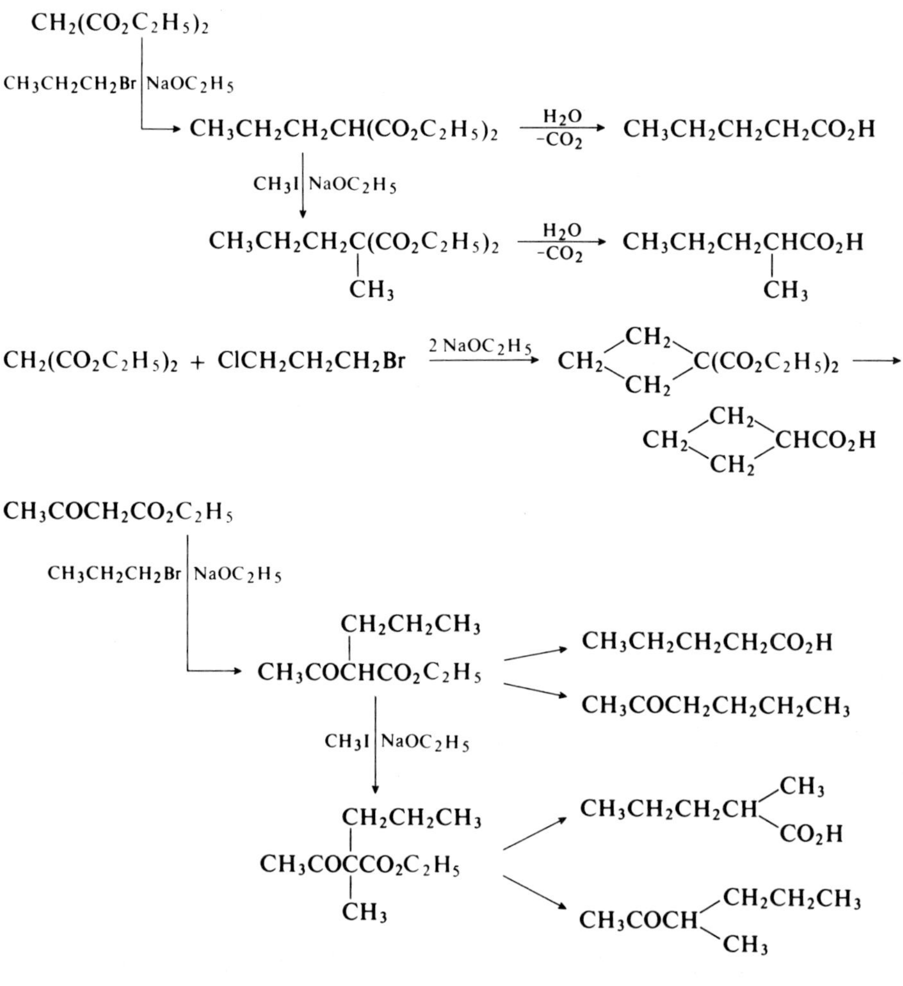

$CH_2(CO_2C_2H_5)_2$

$CH_3CH_2CH_2Br$ | $NaOC_2H_5$

$\longrightarrow CH_3CH_2CH_2CH(CO_2C_2H_5)_2 \xrightarrow[-CO_2]{H_2O} CH_3CH_2CH_2CH_2CO_2H$

CH_3I | $NaOC_2H_5$ $\downarrow$

$CH_3CH_2CH_2\underset{\underset{CH_3}{|}}{C}(CO_2C_2H_5)_2 \xrightarrow[-CO_2]{H_2O} CH_3CH_2CH_2\underset{\underset{CH_3}{|}}{C}HCO_2H$

$CH_2(CO_2C_2H_5)_2 + ClCH_2CH_2CH_2Br \xrightarrow{2\,NaOC_2H_5} CH_2\underset{CH_2}{\overset{CH_2}{<}}\hspace{-6pt}>C(CO_2C_2H_5)_2 \longrightarrow$

$CH_2\underset{CH_2}{\overset{CH_2}{<}}\hspace{-6pt}>CHCO_2H$

$CH_3COCH_2CO_2C_2H_5$

$CH_3CH_2CH_2Br$ | $NaOC_2H_5$

$\longrightarrow CH_3CO\underset{\underset{CH_2CH_2CH_3}{|}}{C}HCO_2C_2H_5$

$\nearrow CH_3CH_2CH_2CH_2CO_2H$

$\searrow CH_3COCH_2CH_2CH_2CH_3$

CH_3I | $NaOC_2H_5$ $\downarrow$

$CH_3CO\underset{\underset{CH_3}{|}}{\overset{\overset{CH_2CH_2CH_3}{|}}{C}}CO_2C_2H_5$

$\nearrow CH_3CH_2CH_2CH\underset{CO_2H}{\overset{CH_3}{<}}$

$\searrow CH_3COCH\underset{CH_3}{\overset{CH_2CH_2CH_3}{<}}$

Fig. 5-9 Malonic ester and acetoacetic ester syntheses.

activated methylene groups (e.g., malonic ester and acetoacetic ester), it is possible through the use of sufficiently strong bases to alkylate simple ketones. For instance, cyclohexanone can be converted to 2-allylcyclohexanone through the action of sodium amide followed by allyl bromide, as illustrated in Fig. 5-10.

A useful variant for the alkylation of simple ketones employs the corresponding enamine (see Fig. 3-8). Just as the enolate anion is ambident (e.g., $-\overset{\ominus}{\underset{|}{C}}-\underset{|}{C}=O \leftrightarrow -\underset{|}{C}=\underset{|}{C}-O^{\ominus}$), so also is the enamine an ambident species (e.g., $-\overset{\ominus}{\underset{|}{C}}-\underset{|}{C}=\overset{\oplus}{N}\!\!< \leftrightarrow -\underset{|}{C}=\underset{|}{C}-N\!\!<$), the charge-separated

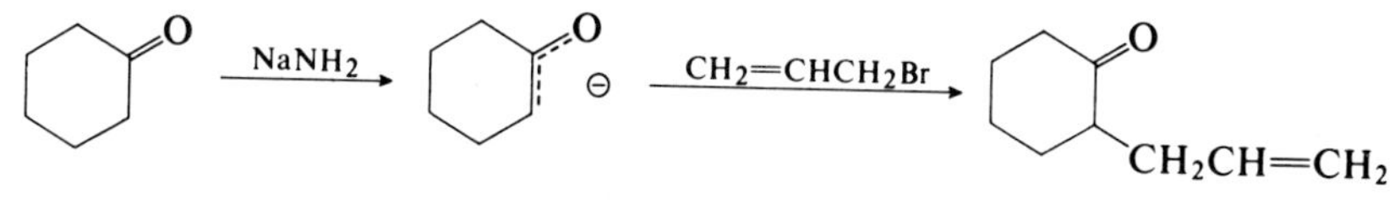

Fig. 5-10 Alkylation of cyclohexanone.

form corresponding to the carbanion form of the enolate, and the enamine form corresponding to the oxanion form. Thus, enamines can undergo N-alkylation or C-alkylation with alkyl halides, and C-alkylation with the appropriate enamine can be made the major reaction pathway. Among the several advantages of this method is the possibility of limiting the reaction to mono-alkylation in cases where direct alkylation has a tendency to proceed further as, for instance, in the example illustrated in Fig. 5-11.

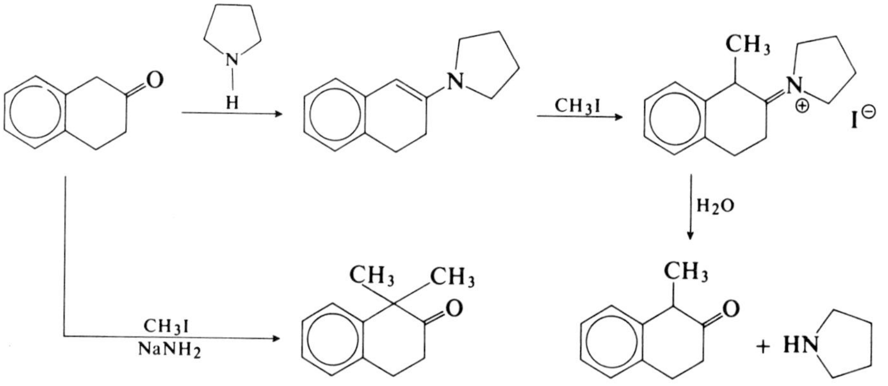

Fig. 5-11 Alkylation of β-tetralone via enamine intermediate.

The second step in the alkylation sequence of the second example in Fig. 5-9 involves intramolecular displacement at a position γ to the carbonyl group. An interesting variation on this scheme occurs in cases where the intramolecularly displaceable group is in a position α' to the carbonyl group. 2-Chlorocyclohexanone, for instance, represents such a case in which the carbanion formed at the α-position has the opportunity of effecting an intramolecular displacement of the chlorine at the α'-position, as illustrated in Fig. 5-12. The cyclopropanone that

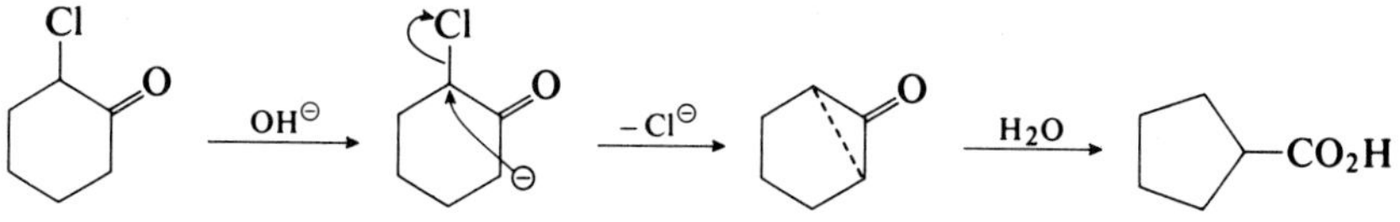

Fig. 5-12 Favorski reaction with 2-chlorocyclohexanone.

would be formed from such a process, however, is very easily cleaved, and the isolated product is a carboxylic acid (in aqueous solution) or an ester (in alcoholic solution). The overall process is known as the "Favorski reaction" and is a characteristic reaction of α-halo ketones.

Still another aspect of intramolecular displacement is seen in those cases where a displaceable group is in a position adjacent to the anionic

center. Systems of the structure $X-\overset{\displaystyle |}{\underset{\displaystyle |}{C}}-\overset{\displaystyle |}{\underset{\displaystyle H}{C}}-\overset{\displaystyle |}{C}=O$ undergo elimination

of HX to form α,β-unsaturated carbonyl compounds, and systems of the

structure $H-\overset{\displaystyle |}{\underset{\displaystyle |}{C}}-C\overset{\displaystyle \diagup O}{\diagdown X}$ undergo elimination of HX to form ketenes, as illustrated by the examples in Fig. 5-13.

$$RCHCH_2COCH_3 \xrightarrow{\ NaOC_2H_5\ } RCH=CHCOCH_3$$
$$\underset{Br}{|}$$

$$CH_3COCH_2CH_2\overset{\oplus}{N}(CH_3)_3 \xrightarrow{\ NaNH_2\ } CH_3COCH=CH_2$$

$$RCH_2C\overset{\diagup O}{\diagdown Cl} \xrightarrow{\ (C_2H_5)_3N\ } RCH=C=O$$

Fig. 5-13 β-Elimination reactions of carbonyl compounds.

The interactions of active methylene anions with carbonyl compounds via direct addition, conjugate addition, and addition-elimination correspond to the aldol condensation, the Michael condensation, and the Claisen reaction and have already been discussed in Chap. 4. The only appropriate supplement to that discussion is to point out that some of those reactions occasionally proceed at the oxygen rather than at the carbon of the active methylene anion. For instance, enol acetates may be prepared from aldehydes and ketones by the action of acetic anhydride and sodium acetate or, more generally, by the action of ketene, as illustrated by the examples in Fig. 5-14.

The replacement of H in $H-Y-\overset{\displaystyle |}{C}=O$ with a halogen atom constitutes another example of an electrophilic displacement at Y. The reaction is confined in its preparative utility to those cases where Y is nitrogen or carbon, for compounds of the structure RCO_2X where X is a halogen atom are extremely unstable. The halogenation of active methylene compounds is a particularly useful reaction and can be effected under base-catalyzed or acid-catalyzed conditions. The base-catalyzed halogenation,

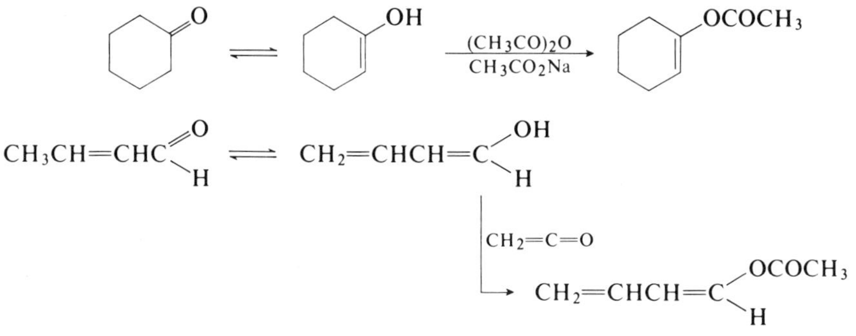

Fig. 5-14 Formation of enol acetates of aldehydes and ketones.

alluded to in the discussion of the haloform reaction (see Fig. 3-26), is interpreted as involving a rate-determining formation of the anion followed by displacement on the halogen molecule. Since the replacement of an α-hydrogen by a halogen atom increases the acidity of the remaining α-hydrogens, subsequent halogenation proceeds even more readily with the halogenated compound than with the starting compound. Thus, cyclohexanone undergoes base-catalyzed bromination to yield the α,α-dibromo compound, as illustrated in Fig. 5-15.

The acid-catalyzed bromination of cyclohexanone, on the other hand, proceeds somewhat more slowly after the introduction of the first bromine atom, making possible the isolation of the monobromo compound, as illustrated in Fig. 5-16. The rate-limiting step in the acid-catalyzed halogenation reaction is known to be the production of the enol, formed as the result of carbonyl protonation followed by α-proton removal (by a basic species such as water). Since the rate of enol formation is dependent, in part, on the extent of carbonyl protonation, the reduction in carbonyl basicity by the electron-withdrawing halogen atom in the α-position reduces the rate of enolization and thereby reduces the rate at which a second halogen is introduced.

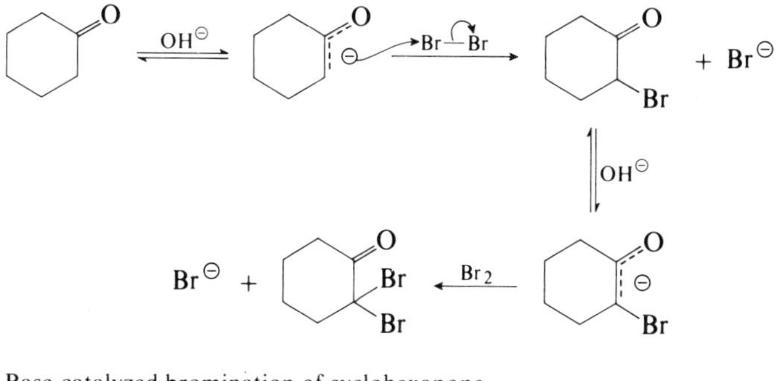

Fig. 5-15 Base-catalyzed bromination of cyclohexanone.

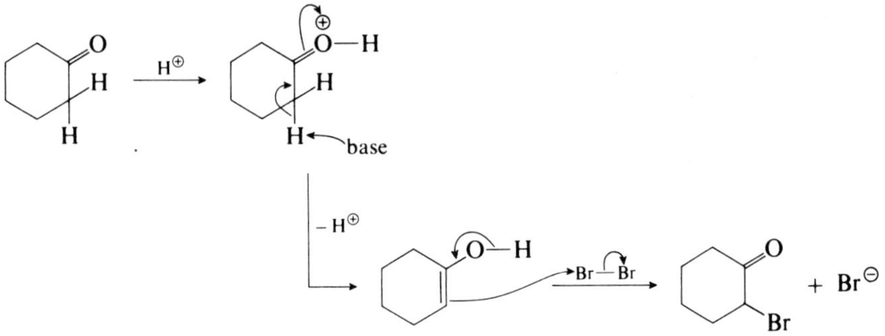

Fig. 5-16 Acid-catalyzed bromination of cyclohexanone.

The intramolecular reactions of active methylene anions discussed so far have been examples of γ-eliminations (e.g., cyclobutane formation in Fig. 5-9 and Favorski reaction in Fig. 5-12), and β-eliminations (e.g., formation of α,β-unsaturated carbonyl compounds and ketenes in Fig. 5-13). Still another possibility for intramolecular elimination exists, namely, α-elimination. The only instances where this occurs with any facility are in carboxylate systems in which the group attached to the carbonyl function is able to easily carry away a pair of electrons. In the majority of cases this is facilitated by imposing a positive charge on

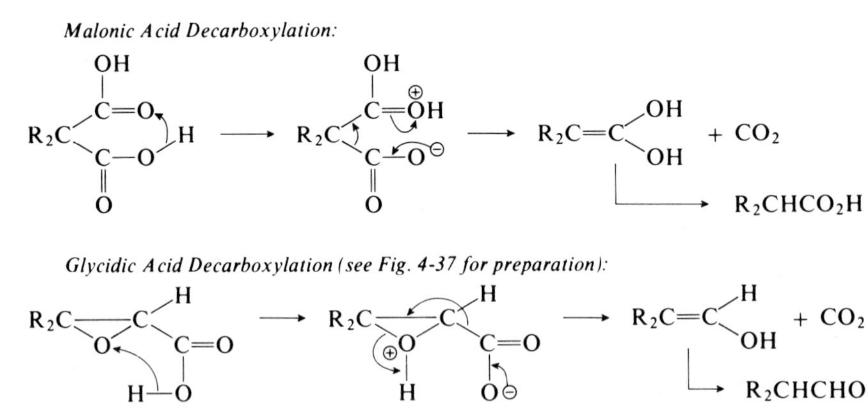

β-Keto Acid Decarboxylation (see Fig. 3-27 for preparation):

Malonic Acid Decarboxylation:

Glycidic Acid Decarboxylation (see Fig. 4-37 for preparation):

Fig. 5-17 Decarboxylation reactions.

the attached group, which is subsequently neutralized as carbon dioxide splits away from the molecule. The several examples of Fig. 5-17 illustrate the process.

PROBLEMS

1. Designate the nucleophilic and electrophilic displacements in the following reactions:

a. 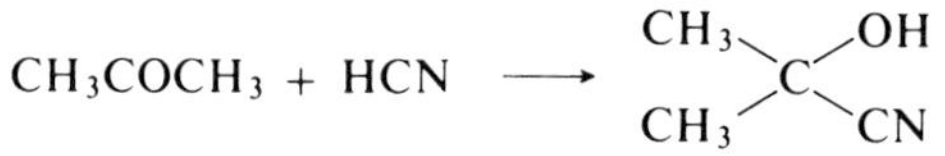 $CH_3COCH_3 + HCN \longrightarrow$

(structure: central C bonded to CH_3, CH_3, OH, CN)

b. $C_6H_5COCH_3 + CH_3MgI \longrightarrow$

(structure: central C bonded to C_6H_5, CH_3, $OMgX$, CH_3)

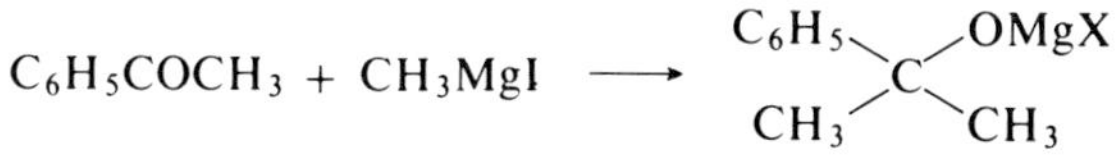

c. $C_6H_5CH{=}CHCO_2C_2H_5 + CH_3NO_2 \longrightarrow C_6H_5CHCH_2CO_2C_2H_5$
$\qquad\qquad\qquad\qquad\qquad\qquad\qquad\qquad\qquad |$
$\qquad\qquad\qquad\qquad\qquad\qquad\qquad\qquad CH_2NO_2$

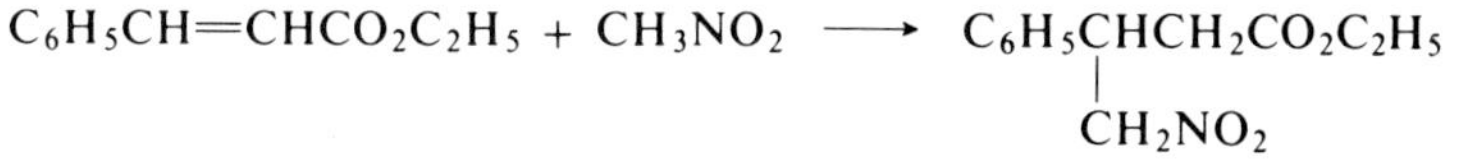

d. 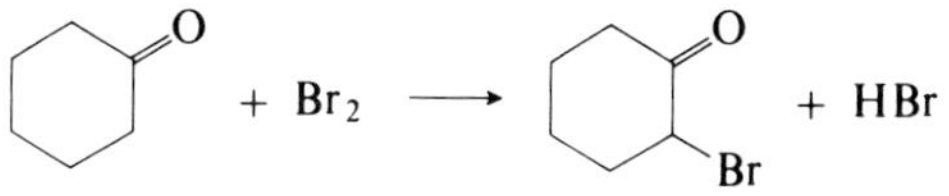 $+ Br_2 \longrightarrow$ $+ HBr$

e. $CH_3COCH_3 + H_2SO_4 \longrightarrow [(CH_3)_2COH]^{\oplus} + HSO_4^{\ominus}$

2. Indicate the reaction or reactions that might be employed to effect the following conversions:

a. 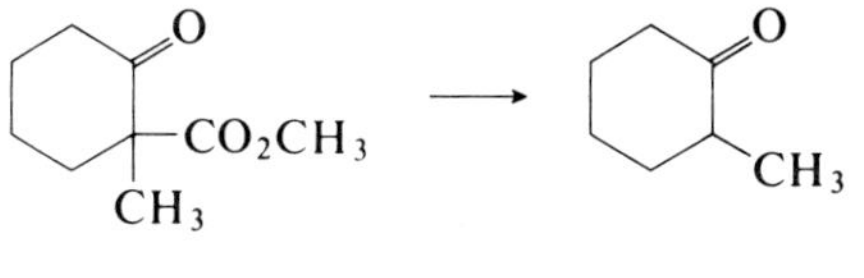 $\longrightarrow$

b. 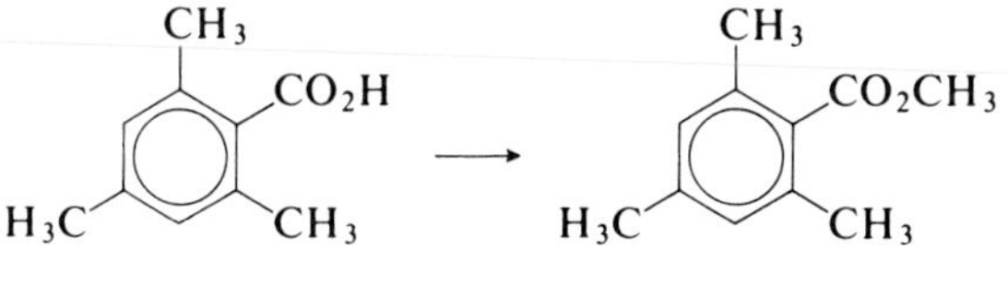 $\longrightarrow$

c. 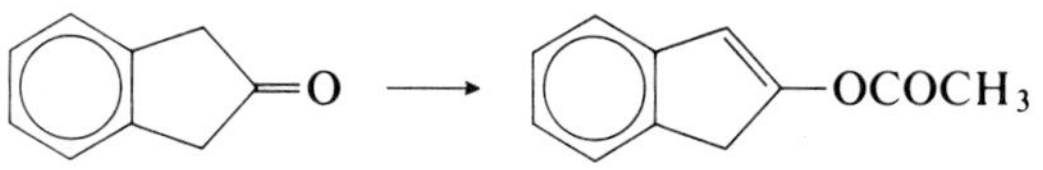 $\longrightarrow$

d. $(C_6H_5)_2C{=}O \longrightarrow (C_6H_5)_2CHCHO$

e. 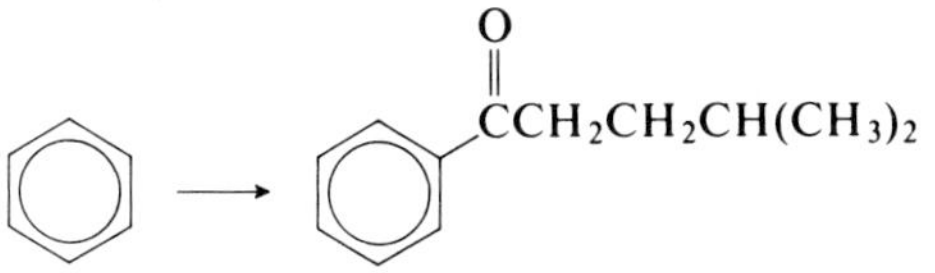 $\longrightarrow$

3. Starting with chemicals available for less than $10 per 100 g, devise syntheses for the following compounds:

a. 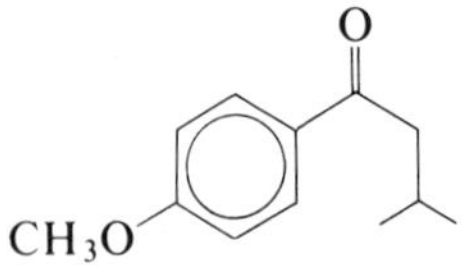
CH_3O—

b. $CH_3CH_2CH_2C(CO_2C_2H_5)_2$
     $|$
   $CH_2CH(CH_3)_2$

c. $CH_3CH_2\overset{O}{\overset{||}{C}}—\overset{CH_2CH_3}{\underset{CH_3}{\overset{|}{\underset{|}{C}}}}CO_2C_2H_5$

d. 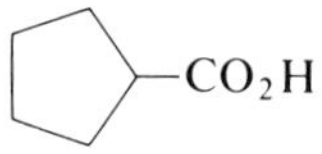
—CO_2H

e. $CH_3\overset{O}{\overset{||}{C}}CH\overset{CH_2C_6H_5}{\underset{CH_2CH=CH_2}{\diagup}}$

f. $C_6H_5COCH=CH_2$

g. $\overset{CH_3}{\underset{CH_3}{\diagup}}CHCH=C=O$

h. $CH_3C(CO_2C_2H_5)_2$
          $|$
         Br

i. $(CH_2)_{10}\overset{CH(CO_2C_2H_5)_2}{\underset{CH(CO_2C_2H_5)_2}{\diagup\diagdown}}$

j. 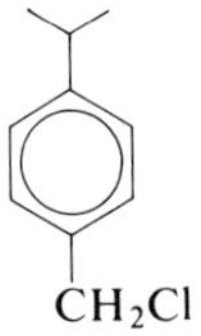
CH_2Cl

SELECTED REFERENCES

Many additional examples of the types of reactions discussed in this chapter are to be found in (a) H. O. House, *Modern Synthetic Reactions,* New York: W. A. Benjamin, Inc., 1965; (b) R. C. Fuson, *Reactions of Organic Compounds: A Textbook for the Advanced Student,* New York: John Wiley & Sons, Inc., 1962; (c) E. E. Royals, *Advanced Organic Chemistry,* Englewood Cliffs, N.J.: Prentice-Hall, Inc., 1954. Detailed discussions of certain of the topics covered in this chapter are to be found in (a) A. S. Kende, "The Favorski Rearrangement," *Organic Reactions,* Vol. 11, p. 261 (1960); (b) A. C. Cope, H. L. Holmes, and H. O. House, "Alkylation of Esters," *Organic Reactions,* Vol. 9, p. 107 (1957); (c) C. R. Hauser, F. W. Swamer, and J. T. Adams, "Acylation of Ketones," *Organic Reactions,* Vol. 8, p. 59 (1954).

Other Reactions
of
Carbonyl Compounds

6.1 OXIDATION-REDUCTION REACTIONS

To segregate some of the reactions of carbonyl compounds and to designate them as oxidation and reduction reactions involves a certain arbitrariness. In addition to the reactions to be discussed in the present section, many of the reactions discussed in previous chapters would also fall in this category. For instance, virtually all of the nucleophilic addition reactions must be viewed as reductions from the standpoint of the carbonyl carbon. Quite clear in this respect is the reaction with hydride ion (see Sec. 3.5), where, in the overall process, two hydrogen atoms are added across the carbon-oxygen double bond. The addition of other groups such as R (via RMgX) is also viewed as reduction in the sense that the electron density at the carbonyl carbon increases as the product forms. Similarly, the substitution of an α-hydrogen by halogen (see Figs. 5-15 and 5-16) must be viewed as an oxidation at the α-carbon atom in the sense that the electron density at that carbon has been diminished by the reaction. That an oxidation has indeed occurred is plainly seen in the hydrolysis of the α-halocarbonyl compound, which leads to an α-hydroxy carbonyl compound; the overall process has involved the conversion

$$H-\overset{|}{\underset{|}{C}}- \rightarrow HO-\overset{|}{\underset{|}{C}}-.$$

Poised as they are in the middle of the oxidation sequence of carbon, carbonyl compounds are capable of either gaining or losing electrons, i.e., of being reduced or oxidized. Thus, aldehydes can be oxidized to carboxylic acids ($RCHO \rightarrow RCO_2H$) or reduced to alcohols ($RCHO \rightarrow RCH_2OH$), hydrocarbons ($RCHO \rightarrow RCH_3$), or diols ($RCHO \rightarrow RCHOHCHOHR$); ketones can be oxidized, with fragmentation of the molecule, to carboxylic acids or reduced to alcohols ($R_2CO \rightarrow R_2CHOH$), hydrocarbons ($R_2CO \rightarrow R_2CH_2$), or diols ($R_2CO \rightarrow R_2C(OH)C(OH)R_2$); carboxylic acids and carboxylic acid derivatives can be reduced to aldehydes (RCOY $\rightarrow$ RCHO) or alcohols (RCOY $\rightarrow$ RCH$_2$OH). The mechanistic aspects of these reactions and the reagents required for effecting them are discussed in detail in another volume of this series.[†]

The only oxidation-reduction reactions that will be discussed in any detail in this section are those in which the carbonyl compound serves both as reductant and oxidant, such processes being termed disproportionation reactions. When non-enolizable aldehydes (principally aromatic aldehydes) are treated with strong aqueous or alcoholic base, one molecule of aldehyde undergoes reduction to the alcohol, while another molecule of aldehyde undergoes oxidation to the acid. This disproportionation, known as the "Cannizzaro reaction," is the result of a nucleophilic addition of hydroxide ion to the aldehyde carbonyl to give a tetrahedral intermediate which can then regenerate the carbonyl function either by expelling hydroxide ion (to revert to aldehyde) or by expelling hydride ion (to go to carboxylic acid). (See Fig. 6-1.) The addition of hydroxide ion and expulsion of hydride ion, another example of nucleophilic addition-elimination (see Fig. 2-15), proceeds because the aldehyde function is a ready acceptor for the expelled hydride ion.[‡] "Crossed Cannizzaro reactions" can be of preparative utility if one of the components is formaldehyde, which, used in excess, acts as the hydride donor and reduces the other aldehyde to the alcohol, e.g., RCHO + HCHO $\rightarrow$ RCH$_2$OH + HCO$_2$H.

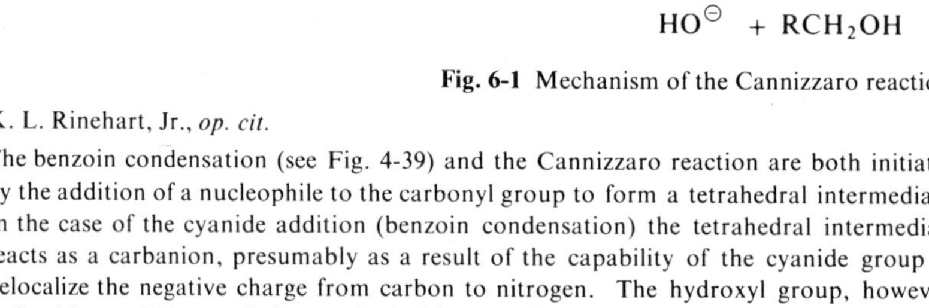

Fig. 6-1 Mechanism of the Cannizzaro reaction.

[†] K. L. Rinehart, Jr., *op. cit.*

[‡] The benzoin condensation (see Fig. 4-39) and the Cannizzaro reaction are both initiated by the addition of a nucleophile to the carbonyl group to form a tetrahedral intermediate. In the case of the cyanide addition (benzoin condensation) the tetrahedral intermediate reacts as a carbanion, presumably as a result of the capability of the cyanide group to delocalize the negative charge from carbon to nitrogen. The hydroxyl group, however, lacks this capability, and the tetrahedral intermediate resulting from hydroxide addition reacts as a hydride donor instead (Cannizzaro reaction). That the cyanide ion adduct can sometimes also react in this fashion is suggested by the following example:

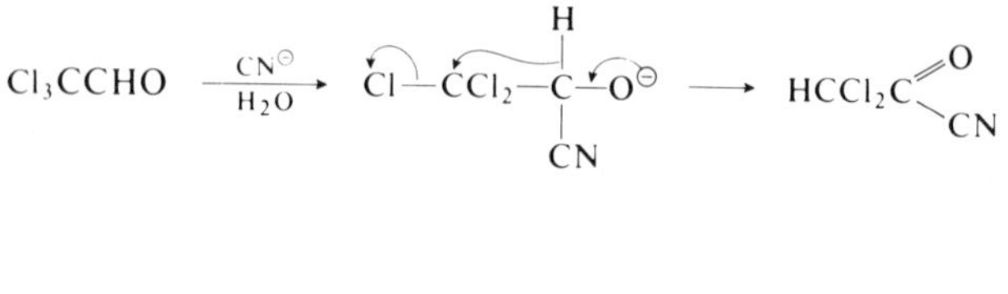

A process with ketones comparable to the Cannizzaro reaction of aldehydes would involve the transfer of a carbanion rather than a hydride ion, e.g., $2 R_2C=O + HO^{\ominus} + H_2O \rightarrow RCO_2H + R_3COH$. While intermolecular examples of this process are rare or unknown, intramolecular examples are provided by the benzilic acid rearrangement. This reaction, characteristic of α-diketones, is initiated by the addition of hydroxide ion to one of the carbonyl groups, as illustrated in Fig. 6-2.

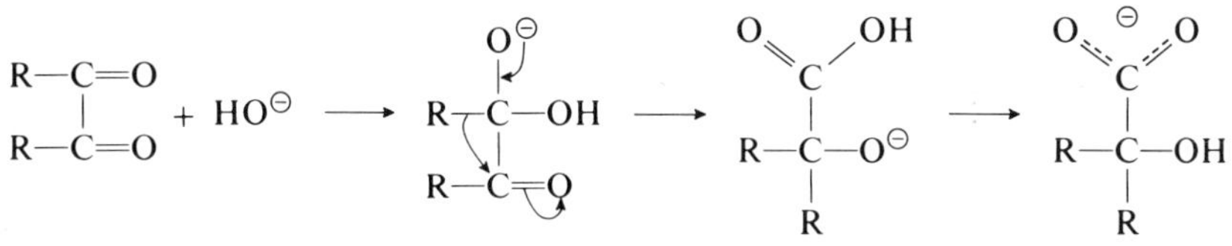

Fig. 6-2 Mechanism of the benzilic acid rearrangement.

The resulting tetrahedral intermediate then collapses (with migration of an R group to the adjacent carbonyl moiety; i.e. an intramolecular nucleophilic addition reaction at this stage) to a carboxylate ion, the stability of which probably furnishes the driving force for the reaction.

6.2 CYCLOADDITION REACTIONS[†]

Aldehydes and ketones can react with certain compounds to give four-membered, five-membered, and six-membered heterocyclic rings in which the carbon and oxygen of the carbonyl group have been assimilated into the ring. Four-membered rings (1,2-cycloaddition) can be formed by the interaction of ketenes with aldehydes or ketones, as illustrated in Fig. 6-3. The resulting β-lactones are quite reactive species and provide useful intermediates in synthesis sequences.

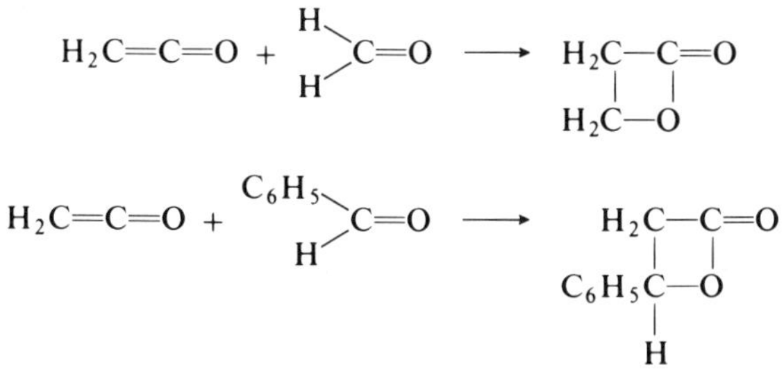

Fig. 6-3 1,2-Cycloaddition reaction.

[†] For an extensive discussion see C. H. DePuy, *Molecular Reactions and Photochemistry* (Englewood Cliffs, N.J.: Prentice-Hall, Inc., in preparation).

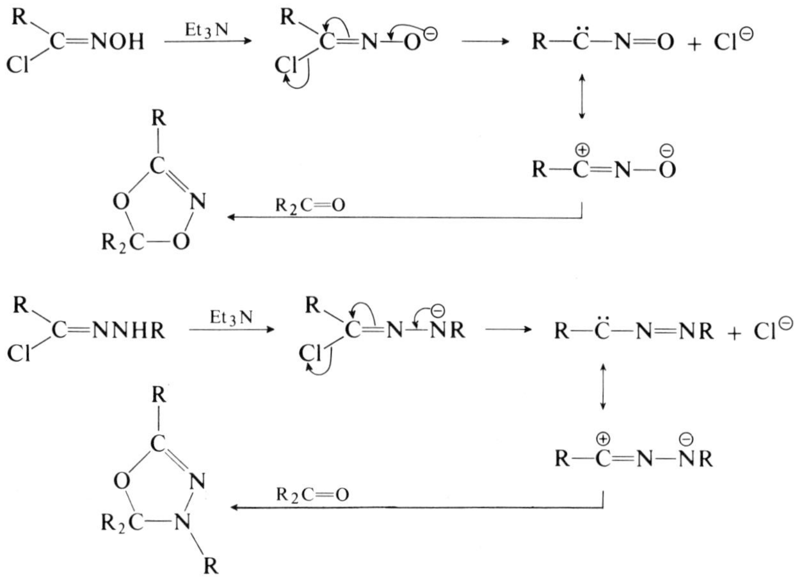

Fig. 6-4 1,3-Cycloaddition reactions (1,3-dipolar additions).

Five-membered rings (1,3-cycloaddition) can be formed from a variety of compounds with aldehydes or ketones. The reactions are usually referred to as 1,3-dipolar additions ("Huisgen reaction") and represent a powerful method for the synthesis of a wide range of five-membered heterocyclic compounds. Two typical examples are shown in Fig. 6-4.

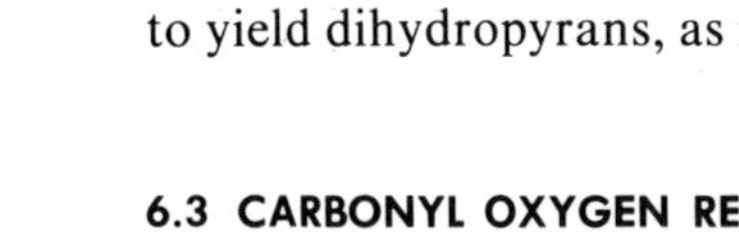

Fig. 6-5 1,4-Cycloaddition reaction.

Although the 1,4-cycloaddition reaction ("Diels-Alder reaction") is best known as a method for preparing six-membered carbocyclic rings, it is also applicable to the synthesis of heterocyclic rings if carbonyl compounds are used as the dienophile. For instance, formaldehyde reacts with dienes to yield dihydropyrans, as illustrated in Fig. 6-5.

6.3 CARBONYL OXYGEN REPLACEMENT REACTIONS

The replacement of the oxygen atom of a carbonyl group by hydrogen (e.g., $R_2C{=}O \rightarrow R_2CH_2$) has already been mentioned (see Sec. 6.1). Replacement of the oxygen atom of a ketone with chlorine can be effected by the action of phosphorus pentachloride; replacement of the oxygen atom of aldehydes, ketones, acids, and carboxylic acid derivatives with fluorine can be effected with sulfur tetrafluoride. The latter reaction appears to be quite general in its application and is a method for prepar-

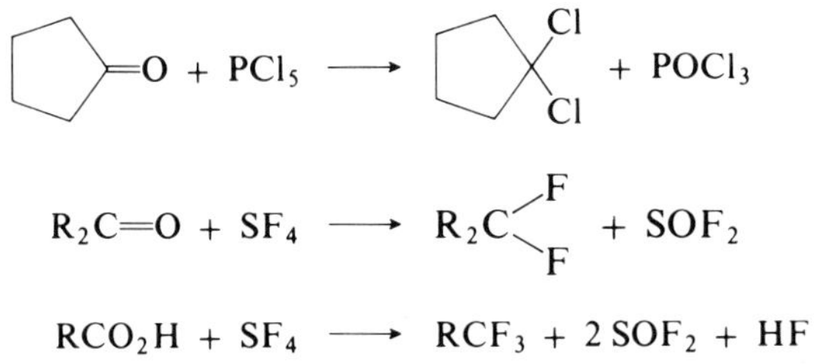

Fig. 6-6 Replacement of carbonyl oxygen with halogen atoms.

ing fluoro compounds that would otherwise be difficult to obtain. Examples of these reactions are illustrated in Fig. 6-6.

6.4 1,2-REARRANGEMENT REACTIONS

The generation of an electron sextet on an atom adjacent to a carbonyl group often leads to rearrangement according to the scheme $RC\begin{smallmatrix}\diagup O \\ \diagdown Y\end{smallmatrix} \rightarrow [O{=}\overset{\oplus}{C}{-}\overset{\ominus}{Y}{-}R] \rightarrow O{=}C{=}Y{-}R$. One example of such a reaction has already been mentioned, namely, the terminal step in the Arndt-Eistert sequence (see Fig. 4-7). In that case, the electron sextet is created on carbon by the elimination of nitrogen from a diazoketone. The rearrangement ("Wolff rearrangement") results in the formation of a ketene which subsequently reacts with the protonic solvent (typically methanol) in which the process is carried out. Another example of this type of reaction occurs in the corresponding nitrogen analogs, where an electron sextet is generated on nitrogen through the loss of molecular nitrogen from an acyl azide ("Curtius rearrangement") or the loss of halogen halide from an N-halo amide ("Hofmann degradation"). In these cases the product of rearrangement is an isocyanate which may be isolable but which usually reacts with the protonic solvent to give a urethan (if the solvent is an alcohol) or a carbamic acid (if the solvent is water). Carbamic acids, however, are unstable and lose carbon dioxide to yield the corresponding amine. Examples of these several reactions are illustrated in Fig. 6-7.

6.5 DECARBONYLATION REACTIONS

Just as the carbonyl unit, i.e., carbon monoxide, can be forced into combination with organic moieties so can it, under appropriate circumstances, be withdrawn from organic combination to form carbon monoxide. The action of strong acid on α-keto acids often results in the extrusion of carbon monoxide; α-polycarbonyl compounds such as α-keto esters and 1,2,3-triketones can be thermally decarbonylated (powdered soft glass is an excellent catalyst); certain cyclic ketones lose carbon mon-

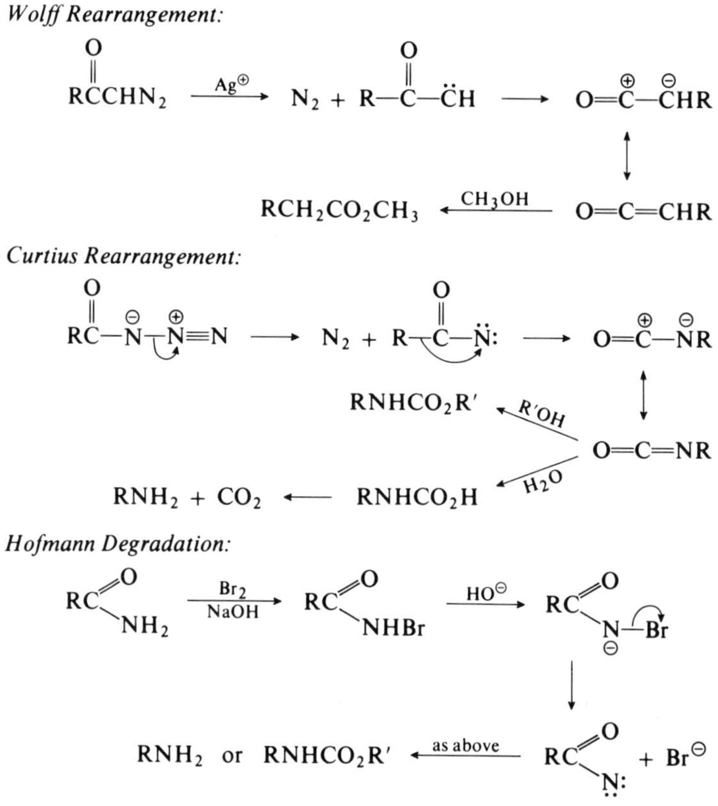

Wolff Rearrangement:

Curtius Rearrangement:

Hofmann Degradation:

Fig. 6-7 1,2-Rearrangements of diazoketones, acyl azides, and amides.

oxide upon irradiation with ultraviolet light. Examples of these several reactions are illustrated in Fig. 6-8.

6.6 POLYMERIZATION REACTIONS

Polymerization requires polyfunctionality of one sort or another. The carbonyl group itself can be considered as a bifunctional entity by virtue of the polarization which creates an electrophilic and a nucleophilic center. Although in the majority of carbonyl compounds this does not lead to a polymerization reaction, in certain cases such a reaction does occur. Lower molecular weight aldehydes, particularly formaldehyde, undergo self-condensation at the carbonyl group to yield cyclic trimers or linear polymers, as illustrated in Fig. 6-9. The commercial plastic "Delrin" is a high molecular weight material prepared by polymerization of formaldehyde followed by a reaction at the ends of the polymer chain. Polyfunctional compounds containing a carbonyl moiety in one or more of the functional groups can often undergo polymerization reactions. For instance, as illustrated in Fig. 6-10, dimethyl terephthalate reacts with

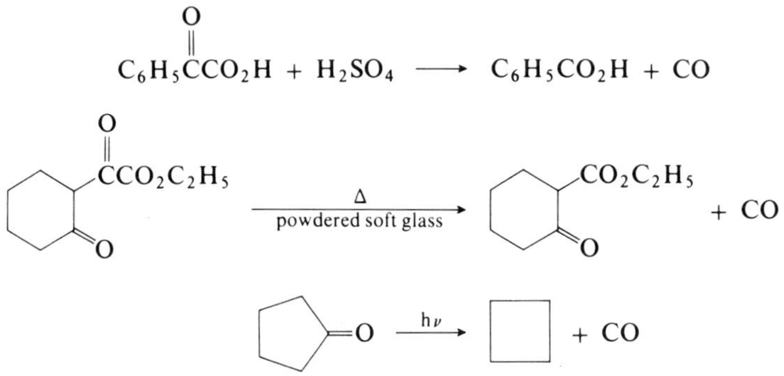

$$C_6H_5\overset{\overset{\displaystyle O}{\|}}{C}CO_2H + H_2SO_4 \longrightarrow C_6H_5CO_2H + CO$$

Fig. 6-8 Decarbonylation reactions.

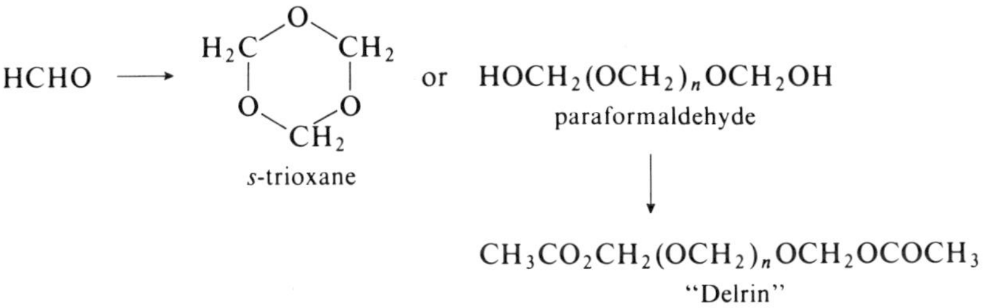

$HCHO \longrightarrow$ s-trioxane or $HOCH_2(OCH_2)_nOCH_2OH$ paraformaldehyde

$$\longrightarrow CH_3CO_2CH_2(OCH_2)_nOCH_2OCOCH_3$$
"Delrin"

Fig. 6-9 Polymerization of formaldehyde.

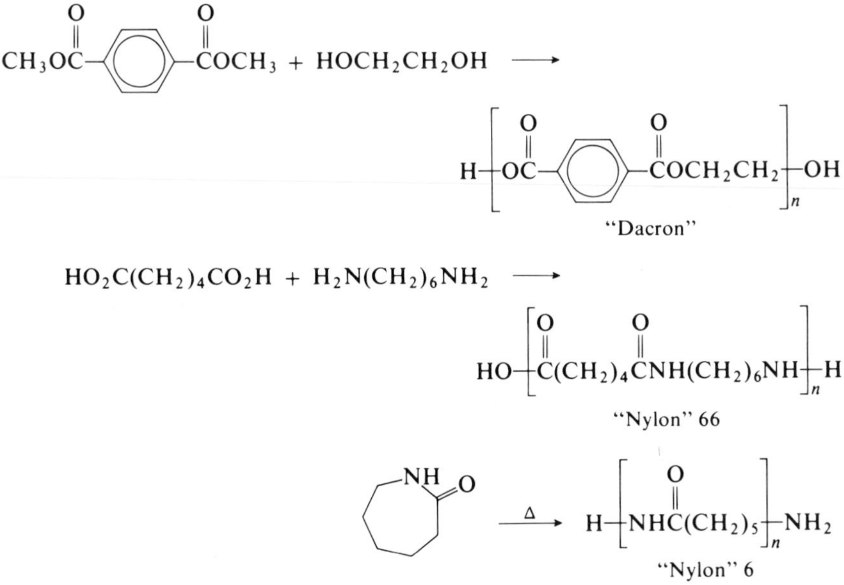

$$CH_3O\overset{\overset{\displaystyle O}{\|}}{C}\text{—}\bigcirc\text{—}\overset{\overset{\displaystyle O}{\|}}{C}OCH_3 + HOCH_2CH_2OH \longrightarrow$$

$$H\text{—}\left[\overset{\overset{\displaystyle O}{\|}}{OC}\text{—}\bigcirc\text{—}\overset{\overset{\displaystyle O}{\|}}{C}OCH_2CH_2\right]_n\text{—}OH$$
"Dacron"

$$HO_2C(CH_2)_4CO_2H + H_2N(CH_2)_6NH_2 \longrightarrow$$

$$HO\text{—}\left[\overset{\overset{\displaystyle O}{\|}}{C}(CH_2)_4\overset{\overset{\displaystyle O}{\|}}{C}NH(CH_2)_6NH\right]_n\text{—}H$$
"Nylon" 66

$$\xrightarrow{\Delta} H\text{—}\left[NH\overset{\overset{\displaystyle O}{\|}}{C}(CH_2)_5\right]_n\text{—}NH_2$$
"Nylon" 6

Fig. 6-10 Polymers from polyfunctional carbonyl compounds.

ethylene glycol to form the polyester known as "Dacron," adipic acid reacts with 1,6-diaminohexane to form a polyamide ("Nylon" 66), and ε-caprolactam undergoes self-condensation to another polyamide ("Nylon" 6).

PROBLEMS

Group A

The widespread occurrence of the carbonyl group in compounds of nature has required the organic chemist to learn its characteristics in his quest to unravel the structures produced by the living cell, an undertaking that has been a major area of organic chemistry for over a century. From the structure of such simple substances as acetic acid and lactic acid (determined more than a hundred years ago), structure proofs have graduated to more complex entities such as the sugars (first worked out by Emil Fischer at the end of the nineteenth century), the steroids (worked out by Wieland, Windaus, and others in the early twentieth century), and certain proteins (e.g., myosin, worked out by Kendrew and Perutz in the present decade), to mention but a few. After one has learned how to take a system apart in such a fashion as to discern its structure, however, he then faces the even more stringent test of learning how to put it back together again. The ability of the chemist to synthesize compounds is a most practical test of his mastery over the molecule. With this thought in mind, the final set of review exercises presents a number of synthesis problems which provide a yardstick against which the reader of this book can measure his mastery of the carbonyl function.

Many natural products have been produced by total synthesis in the laboratory. In the majority of cases, carbonyl reactions have played an important part at some point in the synthesis sequence. The first set of questions, therefore, centers on a few selected examples of such syntheses and asks that the appropriate reaction be indicated wherever a straight arrow appears in the flow sheet. Wavy arrows simply indicate that in some fashion not relevant to the present discussion the conversion of reactant to product was effected.

1. **Equilenin:** This material is the simplest of all of the steroids in having the fewest number of asymmetric centers. As a consequence, it was the first steroid to be totally synthesized. The sequence of reactions employed were those shown in the following flow sheet [Bachmann, Cole, and Wilds, *J. Am. Chem. Soc.*, **62**, 824 (1940)]:

(continued on next page)

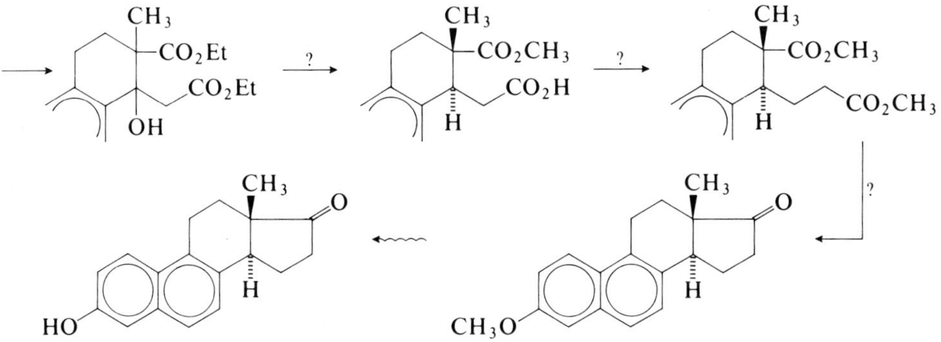

DL-equilenin

2. Lysergic Acid: A disease called ergotism is caused by eating cereal grains, particularly rye, on which has grown a parasitic fungus. The fungal constituents responsible for the disease are called ergot alkaloids and are amides of the compound known as lysergic acid. Even more potent than the naturally occurring amides is lysergic acid diethylamide, which has achieved notoriety for its ability to induce schizophrenic-like symptoms in humans. The synthesis of lysergic acid has been achieved by the following sequence of reactions [Kornfeld, Woodward, et. al., *J. Am. Chem. Soc.,* **78,** 3087 (1956)]:

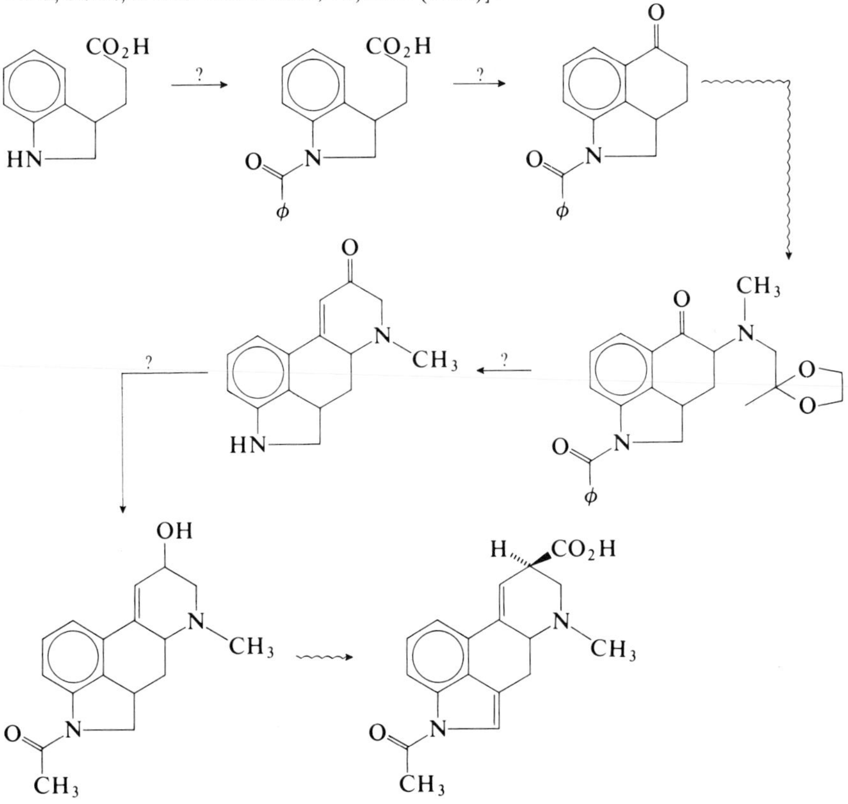

DL-lysergic acid

3. Colchicine: This compound can be obtained by extraction of various portions of the plant known as the autumn crocus. Colchicine has been used for many years as a treatment for gout but is more interesting as a specific mitotic reagent; it interferes with the process of mitosis in such a way as to cause chromosome doubling. One of the recent syntheses of this substance is shown in the following flow sheet [van Tamelen, Spencer, Allen, and Orvis, *Tetrahedron* **14**, 8 (1961)]:

(continued on next page)

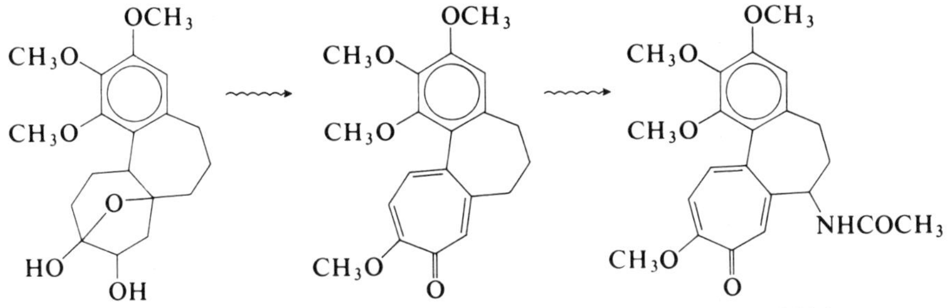

DL-colchicine

4. Longifolene: One of the most structurally convoluted of the sesquiterpenes is the molecule longifolene, isolated from *Pinus longifolia*. The structure of this material was established in 1953 by X-ray techniques, and its total synthesis has been achieved by the reactions shown in the following flow sheet [Corey, Ohno, Mitra, and Vatakencherry, *J. Am. Chem. Soc.*, **86**, 478 (1964)]:

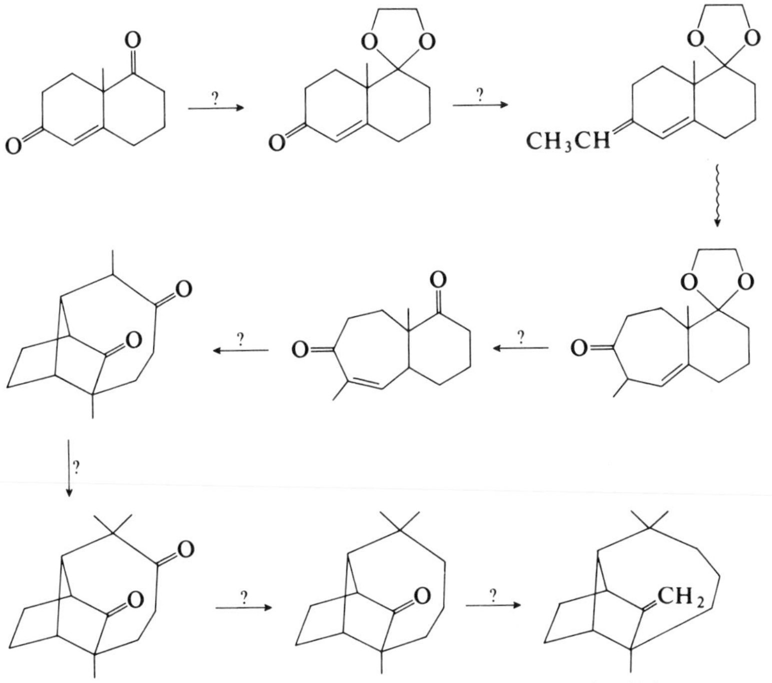

DL-longifolene

Group B

Preparative organic chemistry was referred to in Chap. 3 as the last refuge of the artist-chemist. It, like other areas of chemistry, is sometimes practiced as a pure art form, and the second set of questions engages that practice. It should be kept in mind, however, that "paper syntheses" are intended to represent actual laboratory operation. The aim in the laboratory (or in the industrial plant) is to obtain the maximum amount of product with the minimum input of effort (as represented by man hours and dollars). In designing syntheses for the compounds pictured below, the student should strive for that sequence which uses starting materials available for less than $10 per 100 g.[†] and which involves the minimum input of laboratory effort per gram of product. Like the bridge builder, the artist-chemist must, before all else, design a sequence that will work. If, in addition, he can add a touch of elegance he has served God as well as mammon. The pathway to a particular material is not always immediately apparent. It is usually necessary to dissect the end product in such a fashion that the approach to its synthesis becomes revealed. One should first determine the reaction that might be used in the final step and then proceed to write the structures for the reactants necessary for that step. These compounds should, in turn, be dissected and so on down the line until available starting materials have been reached.

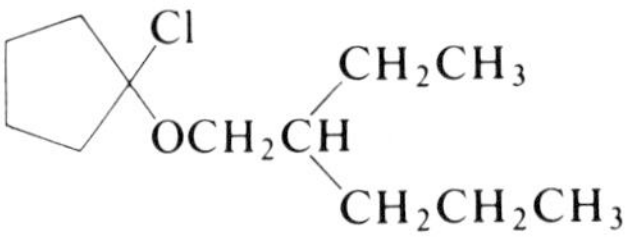

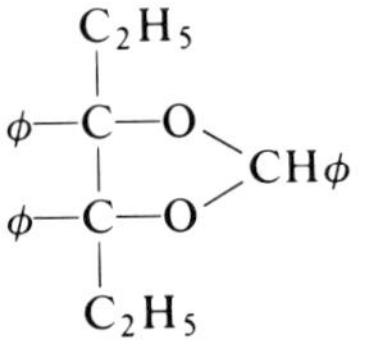

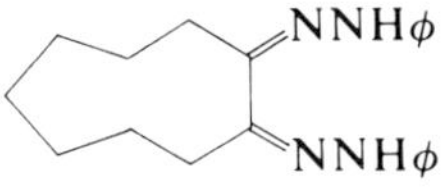

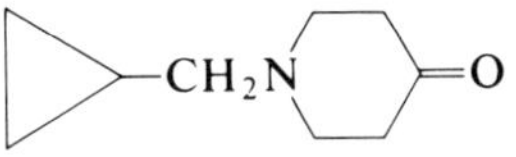

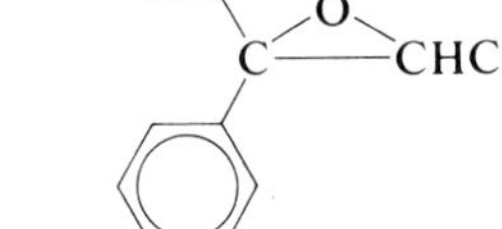

† This figure is, of course, arbitrary but represents a reasonable one for research laboratory operation. For most industrial processes, the starting materials must be a great deal less expensive than this.

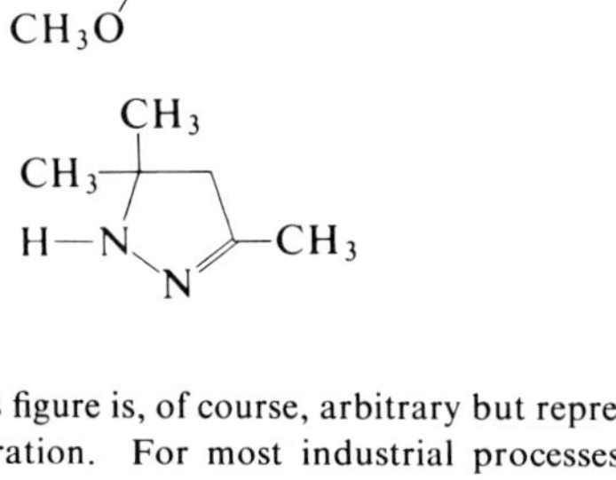

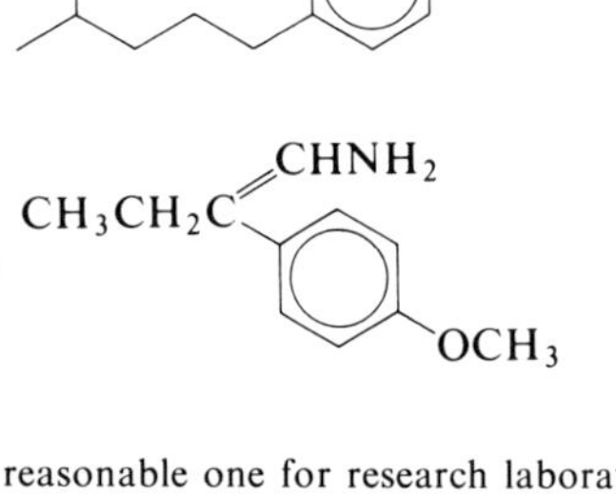

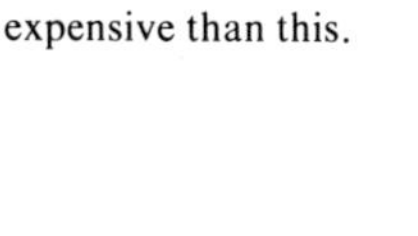

k. 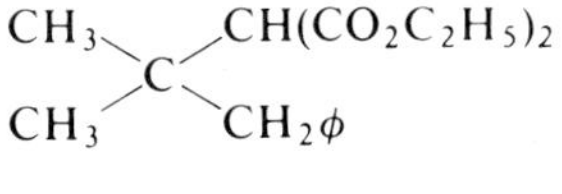
$$CH_3 \diagdown C \diagup CH(CO_2C_2H_5)_2$$
$$CH_3 \diagup C \diagdown CH_2\phi$$

l. 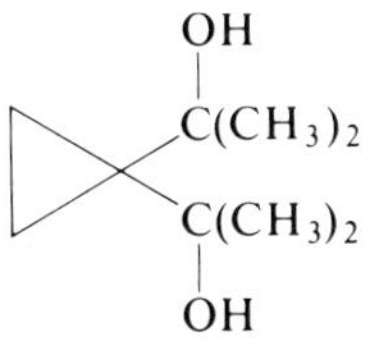
OH
$$C(CH_3)_2$$
$$C(CH_3)_2$$
OH

m. 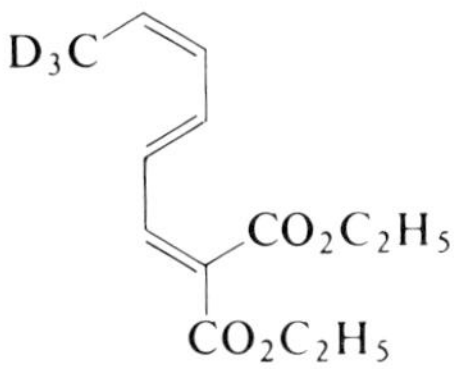
$$D_3C$$
$$CO_2C_2H_5$$
$$CO_2C_2H_5$$

n. 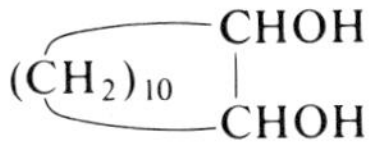 $(CH_2)_{10}$ —CHOH
$|$
—CHOH

o. 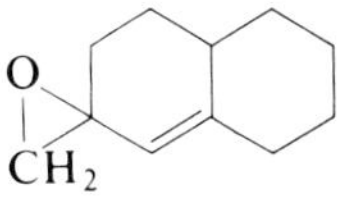 O
$$CH_2$$

p. 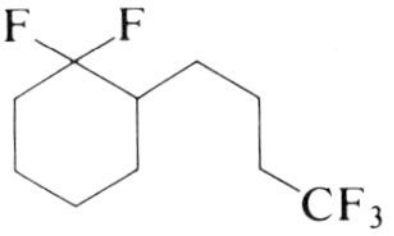
F F
$$CF_3$$

q. 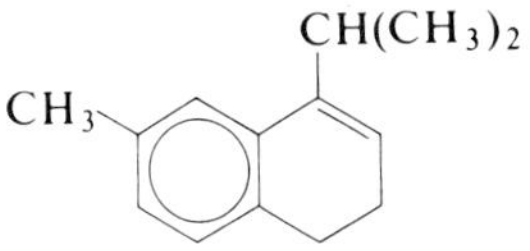
$$CH_3$$
$$CH(CH_3)_2$$

SELECTED REFERENCES

Many additional examples of the types of reactions discussed in this chapter are to be found in R. C. Fuson, *Reactions of Organic Compounds: A Textbook for the Advanced Student,* New York: John Wiley & Sons, Inc., 1962. Detailed discussions of certain of the topics covered in this chapter are to be found in (a) W. S. Ide and J. S. Buck, "The Synthesis of Benzoins," *Organic Reactions,* Vol. 4, p. 269 (1948); (b) P. A. S. Smith, "The Curtius Reaction," *Organic Reactions,* Vol. 3, p. 337 (1946); (c) W. S. Wallis and J. F. Lane, "The Hofmann Reaction," *Organic Reactions,* Vol. 3, p. 267 (1946); (d) T. A. Geissman, "The Cannizzaro Reaction," *Organic Reactions,* Vol. 2, p. 94 (1944).

Summary
of
Synthesis Methods
for
Carbonyl Compounds

A systematic summary of synthesis methods for aldehydes, ketones, carboxylic acids, and carboxylic acid derivatives is presented in this section. In those cases where illustrative examples have already been cited in earlier sections of the book, reference to the appropriate Fig. is given. In other cases, examples taken from *Organic Syntheses* are provided for illustration. *Organic Syntheses* is a yearly publication which includes synthesis methods that have been carefully checked and are known to be reliable. The citations to the *Organic Syntheses* methods appear as "O.S." followed by a Roman numeral to indicate the number of the Collective Volume or an Arabic numeral to indicate the number of the yearly volume, these numbers then followed by the page number. The student is urged to consult these references for detailed information concerning the reactions.

Preparation of aldehydes by replacement of a C-hetero atom by C—H

1. RCOCl $\longrightarrow$ RCHO (see Fig. 3-32)

O.S. III, 551

2. $RCN \longrightarrow RCHO$

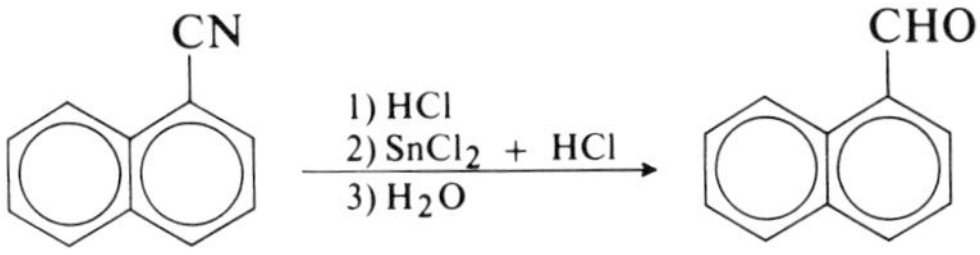
CN
1) HCl
2) SnCl2 + HCl
3) H2O
CHO

O.S. III, 626

Preparation of aldehydes and ketones by replacement of C—H by C—O (oxidation reactions)

1. $RCH_2OH \rightarrow RCHO$

$$CH_3CH_2CH_2OH \xrightarrow[H_2SO_4]{K_2Cr_2O_7} CH_3CH_2CHO$$ O.S. II, 541

$$HC{\equiv}CCH_2OH \xrightarrow{CrO_3} HC{\equiv}CCHO$$ O.S. IV, 813

2. $R_2CHOH \longrightarrow R_2C{=}O$

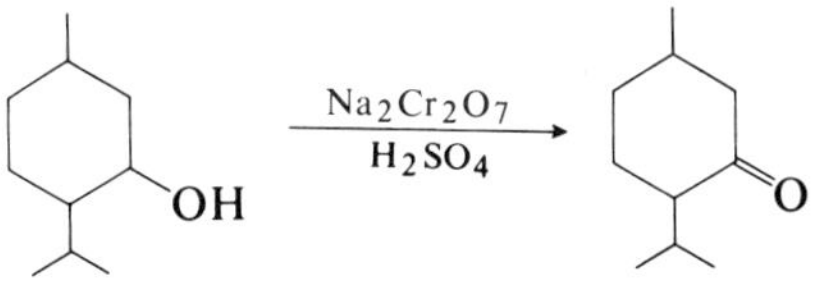
OH
Na2Cr2O7
H2SO4
O

O.S. I, 340

3. $RR'CHNO_2 \longrightarrow RR'C{=}O$ (see Fig. 4-27)

4. $RCOCH_2R' \longrightarrow RCOCOR'$

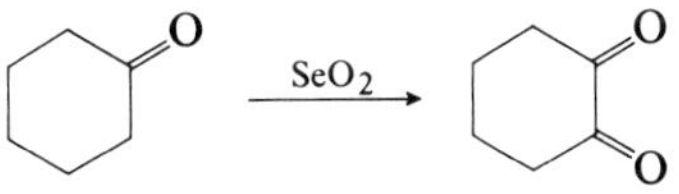
O
SeO2
O
O

O.S. IV, 229

5. $ArCH_2X \longrightarrow ArCHO$

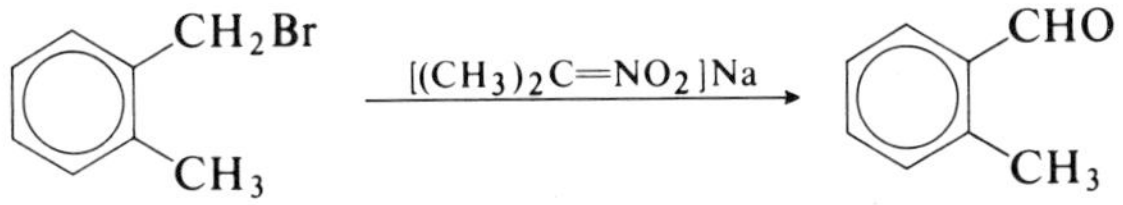
CH2Br
CH3
[(CH3)2C=NO2]Na
CHO
CH3

O.S. IV, 932

6. $ArCH_3 \longrightarrow ArCHO$

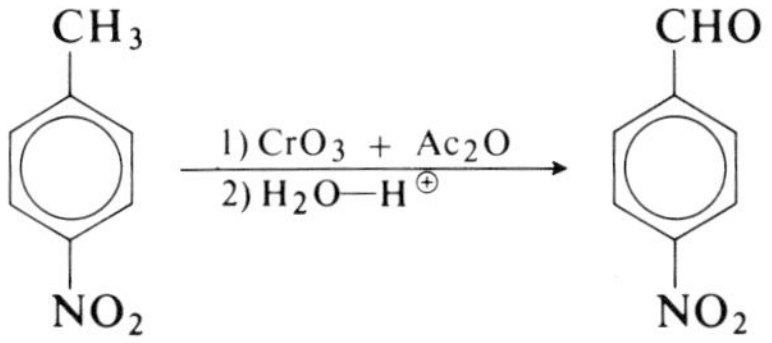
CH3
NO2
1) CrO3 + Ac2O
2) H2O—H⊕
CHO
NO2

O.S. II, 441

Preparation of aldehydes and ketones by C—C bond formation

1. RCN $\longrightarrow$ RCOR' (see Fig. 4-9)

2. RCOCl $\longrightarrow$ RCOR' (see Fig. 4-21)

3. RCO$_2$H $\longrightarrow$ RCOR' (see Fig. 4-22)

4. RCOY $\longrightarrow$ RCOCCOR' (see Figs. 4-32, 4-33, 4-34, 4-35, 4-40)

5. ArH $\longrightarrow$ ArCOR via RCOCl (see Figs. 5-4 and 5-5)

6. ArH $\longrightarrow$ ArCOR via (RCO)$_2$O (see Fig. 5-5)

7. ArH $\longrightarrow$ ArCOR via RCO$_2$H (see Fig. 5-5)

8. ArH $\longrightarrow$ ArCHO via CO + HCl

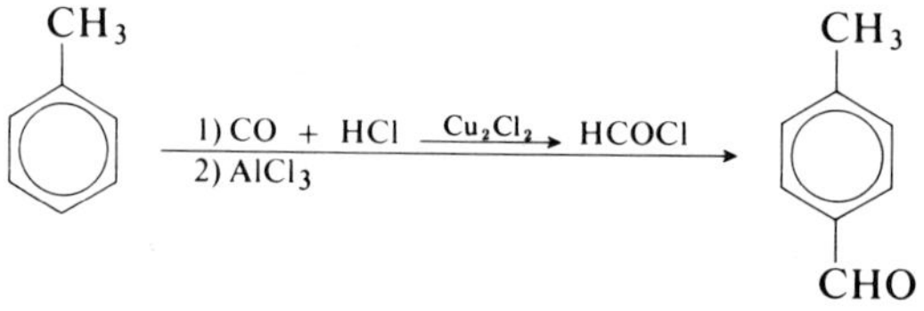

O.S. II, 583

9. ArH $\longrightarrow$ ArCHO via N-methylformanilide

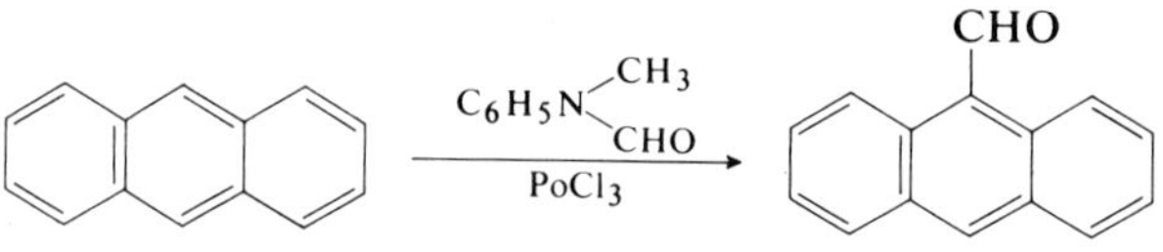

O.S. III, 98

10. RMgX $\longrightarrow$ RCHO

C$_5$H$_{11}$MgBr + CH(OEt)$_3$ $\longrightarrow$

C$_5$H$_{11}$CH(OEt)$_2$ $\xrightarrow{\text{H}_2\text{O}-\text{H}^{\oplus}}$ C$_5$H$_{11}$CHO   O.S. II, 323

11. RCOR $\longrightarrow$ RCOCHRR' via RCHN$_2$ (see Figs. 4-2 and 4-3)

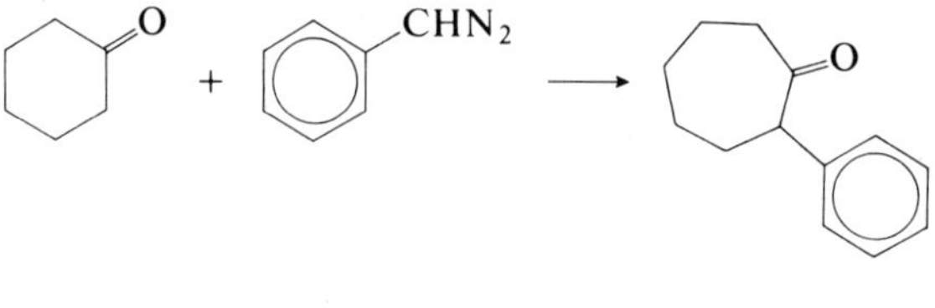

O.S. IV, 780

12. CH$_2$=C=O $\longrightarrow$ CH$_3$COR (see Fig. 3-14)

Preparation of aldehydes and ketones by C—C bond cleavage

1. $R_2C{=}CR_2 \longrightarrow R_2C{=}O$

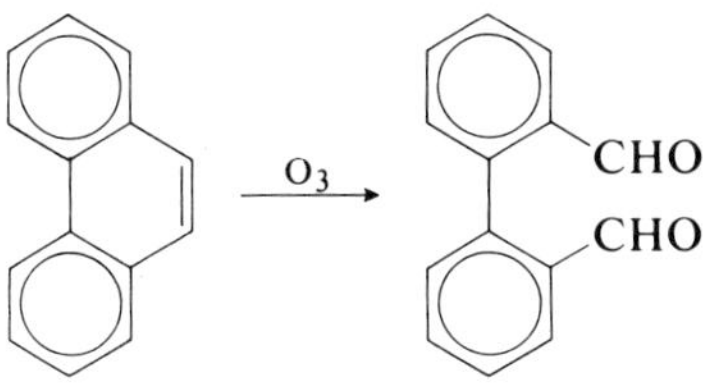

O.S. **41**, 41

2.
$$\underset{\underset{OH}{|}}{R_2C}{-}\underset{\underset{OH}{|}}{CR_2} \to R_2C{=}O$$

$$\underset{\underset{HOCHCO_2C_4H_9}{|}}{HOCHCO_2C_4H_9} \xrightarrow{Pb(OAc)_4} 2\ \underset{\underset{CO_2C_4H_9}{|}}{CHO}$$

O.S. IV, 124

3. $R_2C\underset{O}{\diagdown}CRCO_2Et \to R_2CHCOR$ (see Fig. 5-17)

$$C_6H_5\underset{\underset{O}{\diagdown}}{\overset{\overset{CH_3}{|}}{C}}{-}CHCO_2Et \xrightarrow[\text{2) HCl}]{\text{1) } C_2H_5ONa} C_6H_5\overset{\overset{CH_3}{|}}{C}HCHO$$

O.S. III, 733

4. $RCOCHCO_2Et \to RCOCH_2R'$ (see Figs. 3-27 and 5-9)
   $\underset{\underset{R'}{|}}{}$

$$CH_3COCH_2CO_2Et \xrightarrow[NaOEt]{C_4H_9Br} \underset{\underset{C_4H_9}{|}}{CH_3COCHCO_2Et} \xrightarrow[\text{2) } H_2SO_4]{\text{1) NaOH}}$$

$$\overset{\overset{O}{\|}}{CH_3C}(CH_2)_4CH_3 \qquad \text{O.S. I, 351}$$

Preparation of aldehydes and ketones by rearrangement and hydration reactions

1. $R_2C\underset{O}{\diagdown}CR_2 \to R_3CCOR$

$$C_6H_5CH\underset{O}{\diagdown}CHC_6H_5 \xrightarrow{BF_3} \underset{C_6H_5}{\overset{C_6H_5}{\diagup}}CHCHO$$

O.S. IV, 375

2. $R_2\overset{\underset{\displaystyle |}{OH}}{C}-\overset{\underset{\displaystyle |}{OH}}{C}R_2 \rightarrow R_3CCOR$

$$C_6H_5\overset{\underset{\displaystyle |}{C_6H_5}}{\underset{\underset{\displaystyle OH}{|}}{C}}-\overset{\underset{\displaystyle |}{C_6H_5}}{\underset{\underset{\displaystyle OH}{|}}{C}}C_6H_5 \xrightarrow{H^{\oplus}} C_6H_5\overset{\underset{\displaystyle |}{C_6H_5}}{\underset{\underset{\displaystyle C_6H_5}{|}}{C}}-C\overset{\displaystyle O}{\underset{\displaystyle C_6H_5}{}}$$

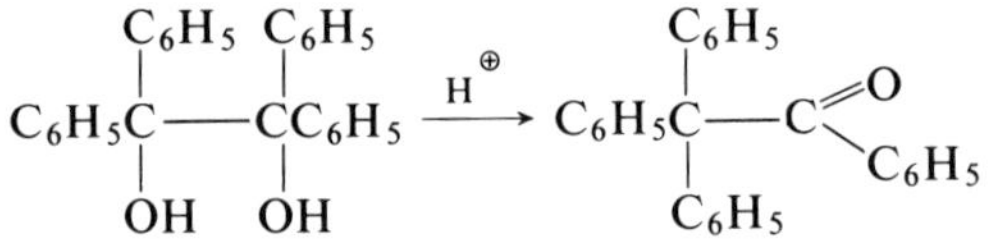

O.S. I, 462

3. $RC{\equiv}CR \rightarrow RCH_2COR$

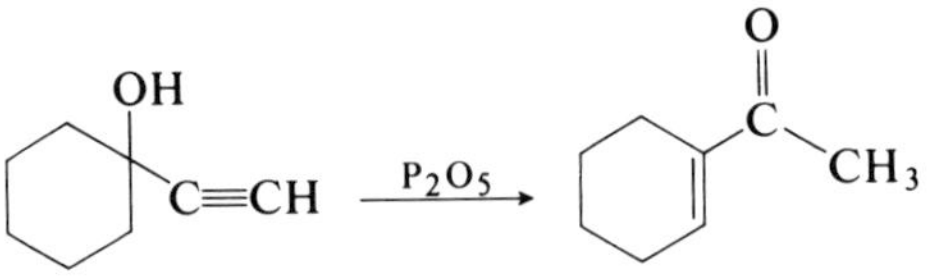

O.S. III, 22

Preparation of carboxylic acids by replacement of C—H by C—O (oxidation reactions)

1. $RCH_2OH \rightarrow RCO_2H$ (see Fig. 3-4)

$$ClCH_2CH_2CH_2OH \xrightarrow{HNO_3} ClCH_2CH_2CO_2H$$

O.S. I, 168

2. $RCHO \rightarrow RCO_2H$

$$C_6H_{13}CHO \xrightarrow{KMnO_4} C_6H_{13}CO_2H$$

O.S. II, 315

3. $ArCH_3 \rightarrow ArCO_2H$

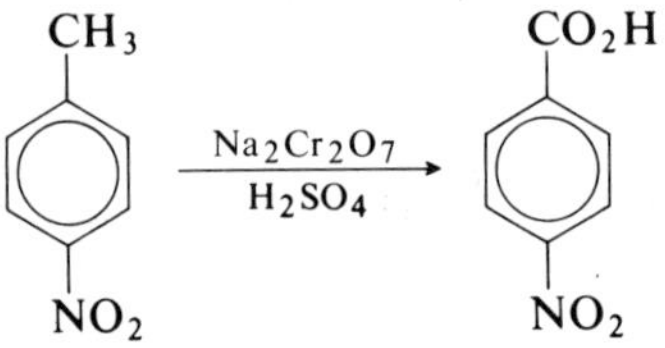

O.S. I, 392

Preparation of carboxylic acids by C—C bond formation

1. $RMgX \rightarrow RCO_2H$ (see Fig. 4-13)

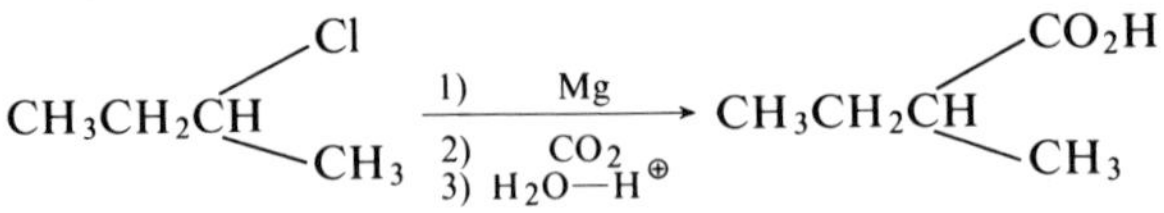

O.S. I, 361

2. $RCHO \rightarrow RCH{=}CHCO_2H$ (see Fig. 4-29)

$$CH_3CH{=}CHCHO + CH_2(CO_2H)_2 \rightarrow CH_3CH{=}CHCH{=}CHCO_2H$$

O.S. III, 783

3. $R_2CO \rightarrow R_2C{=}CHCO_2H$ (see Fig. 4-29)

4. $R_3CH \rightarrow R_3CCO_2H$

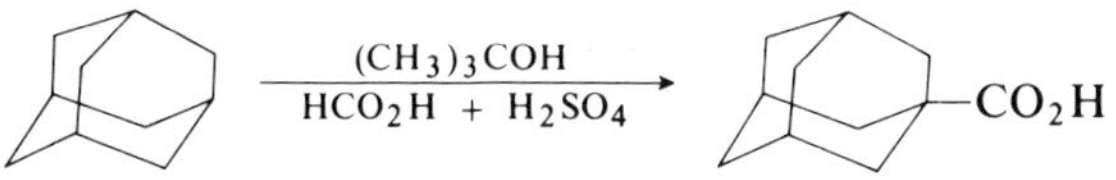

$$\xrightarrow[\text{HCO}_2\text{H} + \text{H}_2\text{SO}_4]{(CH_3)_3COH}$$

—CO_2H O.S. **44**, 1

Preparation of carboxylic acids by C—C bond cleavage

1. $R_2CHOH \rightarrow RCO_2H$

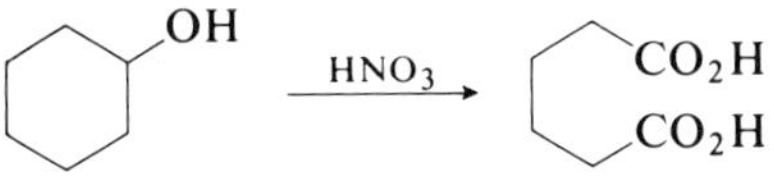

$$\xrightarrow{\text{HNO}_3}$$

O.S. I, 18

2. $R_2CO \rightarrow RCO_2R$ (see Fig. 3-28)

3. $RCOCH_3 \rightarrow RCO_2H$ (see Fig. 3-26)

$$\underset{CH_3}{\overset{CH_3}{\diagdown}}C{=}CHCOCH_3 \xrightarrow[\text{KOH}]{\text{Cl}_2} \underset{CH_3}{\overset{CH_3}{\diagdown}}C{=}CHCO_2H$$

O.S. III, 302

4. $RCH{=}CHR \rightarrow RCO_2H$

$$CH_3(CH_2)_5\underset{\underset{CH_3}{|}}{C}HCH_2CH{=}CH(CH_2)_7CO_2H \xrightarrow{\text{KMnO}_4} HO_2C(CH_2)_7CO_2H$$

O.S. II, 53

5. $RCH(CO_2R)_2 \rightarrow RCH_2CO_2H$ (see Fig. 5-9)

$$CH_2(CO_2Et)_2 \xrightarrow[\text{NaOEt}]{CH_3CH_2CHBrCH_3} CH_3CH_2\underset{\underset{CH_3}{|}}{C}HCH(CO_2Et)_2$$

O.S. II, 416

$$\downarrow \begin{array}{l} \text{1) NaOH} \\ \text{2) H}_2\text{SO}_4 \end{array}$$

$$CH_3CH_2\underset{\underset{CH_3}{|}}{C}HCH_2CO_2H$$

6. $CH_3COCHRCO_2Et \rightarrow RCH_2CO_2H$ (see Fig. 5-9)

Preparation of carboxylic acids by rearrangement reactions

1. $RCOCHN_2 \rightarrow RCH_2CO_2H$ (see Figs. 4-8 and 6-7)

2. $R\overset{O}{\overset{||}{C}}{-}\overset{O}{\overset{||}{C}}R \rightarrow R_2C\overset{\diagup OH}{\underset{\diagdown CO_2H}{}}$ (see Fig. 6-2)

$$C_6H_5\overset{O}{\underset{}{C}}-\overset{O}{\underset{}{C}}C_6H_5 \xrightarrow[\text{2) } H^{\oplus}]{\text{1) NaOH}} \begin{array}{c} C_6H_5 \\ \diagdown \\ C_6H_5 \end{array} \overset{OH}{\underset{CO_2H}{C}}$$ O.S. I, 89

3. $RCHO \rightarrow RCO_2H + RCH_2OH$ (see Fig. 6-1)

O.S. I, 276

$\xrightarrow[\text{2) } H^{\oplus}]{\text{1) NaOH}}$ furyl-CO_2H + furyl-CH_2OH

4. $R\overset{Cl}{\underset{}{C}}HC\overset{O}{\underset{R}{\diagup}} \rightarrow R_2CHCO_2H$ (see Fig. 5-12)

Preparation of carboxylic acids by hydrolysis reactions

1. $RCOY \rightarrow RCO_2H$ where Y = halogen, OR, OAr, and NR_2
(see Figs. 3-22 and 3-23)

2. $RCN \rightarrow RCO_2H$ (see Fig. 4-9)

-CN $\xrightarrow[\text{2) } H_2SO_4]{\text{1) } H_2O-NaOH}$ -CO_2H O.S. III, 221

3. $R_2C=C=O \rightarrow R_2CHCO_2H$ (see Fig. 3-14)

Preparation of carboxylic acid derivatives

1. $RCO_2H \longrightarrow RCOCl$ (see Fig. 3-17)

2. $RCO_2H \longrightarrow RCO_2R$ (see Figs. 3-21 and 5-6)

3. $RCO_2H \longrightarrow RCO_2OR$ (see Figs. 3-18 and 3-36)

4. $RCO_2H \longrightarrow RCONR_2$ (see Fig. 3-36)

5. $RCOCl \longrightarrow RCO_2R$ (see Fig. 3-18)

6. $RCOCl \longrightarrow RCONR_2$ (see Fig. 3-18)

7. $RCOCl \longrightarrow RCO_2OR$ (see Fig. 3-18)

8. $(RCO_2)_2O \longrightarrow RCO_2R$ (see Figs. 3-18 and 5-14)

9. $(RCO)_2O \longrightarrow RCONR_2$ (see Figs. 3-18 and 3-19)

10. $RCO_2R \longrightarrow RCONR_2$ (see Fig. 3-20)

11. $RCO_2R \longrightarrow RCO_2R'$ (see Figs. 3-24 and 3-36)

12. $R_2C=C=O \longrightarrow R_2CHCO_2R$ (see Fig. 3-14)

13. $R_2C=C=O \longrightarrow R_2CHCO_2OR$ (see Fig. 3-14)

14. $R_2C=C=O \longrightarrow R_2CHCONR_2$ (see Fig. 3-14)

15. $RCOCHN_2 \longrightarrow RCH_2CO_2R$ (see Fig. 4-8)

16. $RMgX \longrightarrow RCONR_2$ (see Fig. 4-13)